The Institute of Bioloᶜ
Studies in Biology no.

Chloroplasts and Mitochondria

by Michael Tribe Ph.D., M.I.Biol.
Lecturer in Biological Sciences, University of Sussex
and
Peter Whittaker Ph.D.
Lecturer in Biological Sciences, University of Sussex

Edward Arnold

First published 1972
by Edward Arnold (Publishers) Limited,
25 Hill Street,
London, W1X 8LL

Reprinted 1974
Reprinted 1975

Boards edition ISBN: 0 7131 2337 0
Paper edition   ISBN: 0 7131 2338 9

Printed in Great Britain by
The Camelot Press Ltd, Southampton

General Preface to the Series

It is no longer possible for one textbook to cover the whole field of Biology and to remain sufficiently up to date. At the same time students at school, and indeed those in their first year at universities, must be contemporary in their biological outlook and know where the most important developments are taking place.

The Biological Education Committee, set up jointly by the Royal Society and the Institute of Biology, is sponsoring, therefore, the production of a series of booklets dealing with limited biological topics in which recent progress has been most rapid and important.

A feature of the series is that the booklets indicate as clearly as possible the methods that have been employed in elucidating the problems with which they deal. Wherever appropriate there are suggestions for practical work for the student. To ensure that each booklet is kept up to date, comments and questions about the contents may be sent to the author or the Institute.

1971

INSTITUTE OF BIOLOGY
41 Queen's Gate
London, S.W.7

Preface

The subject matter of this booklet has been chosen in a particularly active area of research, in which rapid changes have taken place in the last ten years. We have not attempted to cover every aspect of photosynthesis and respiration, as these are dealt with in more detail elsewhere (see references at the back of the book), but we have tried to emphasize the problems of energy conservation in relation to the structure and function of organelles. Although we have tried to present an up-to-date outline of our subject, there is considerable speculation about certain problems, and many differences of opinion. The student should appreciate that this is a healthy, thought-provoking situation, even though confusing at times. In addition, he or she should appreciate that many of the currently accepted ideas present here, may in five or ten years time have changed considerably. In view of this we have included an historical evaluation of events leading up to the present state of knowledge to provide perspective to our theme.

We have given some practical details for making crude preparations of chloroplasts and mitochondria, which we hope may be useful as a starting point for those students wishing to pursue special studies in this field.

Brighton, 1971

M.T.
P.W.

Contents

The Need for an Energy Conserving System

1.1 Why do we need an energy conserving system?

The Principle of the Conservation of Energy is one of the most important known to science. It states that energy is neither created nor destroyed, but can nevertheless be transformed from one form to another. It is paramount in living systems, because energy must be available to do work. However, if we try to light a 12 V bulb with a 1 V accumulator, the bulb will not light because the potential of chemical energy in this case is not high enough to power the process. In other words, we require an accumulator with more cells or a higher potential energy source. Again, if we use the same bulb with a 12 V accumulator, light will be produced, but not indefinitely unless the accumulator is frequently recharged. This analogy brings home the point that living systems have to be frequently 'recharged' in order to maintain themselves in the higher energy state. However, there is the difference that living systems are recharged more or less continuously and this can be likened to an accumulator doing work while on charge.

From another important physical law, that of entropy, we know that all systems whether living or non-living tend towards the lowest energy state; i.e. there is an increase in the randomness of systems or disorder, and hence an increase in entropy. To put it bluntly, most living things are in the lowest (and stablest) energy state when they die and decompose, thus dispersing their component atoms, with the result that there is an increase in entropy.

Living organisms are certainly unusual, but they do not possess, as was once thought, some mysterious 'vital force' which enables them to do work contrary to physical laws. The real difference between the living and the non-living is that the processes which go on in living cells enable the organism to maintain a higher energy state. Such a state is more orderly, and thus gives rise to a decrease in entropy.

To get water from an underground reservoir into a storage tank above ground, the engineer uses a pump. The pump performs work and expends energy in maintaining the head of water, but once the fuel supply to the pump, or the pump itself, breaks down, the water cannot be raised to the new level. The situation is very similar in living systems. Here again an energy input (e.g. sunlight or food) is essential to generate energy in cells, so that the input of energy at least balances output. Once this system breaks down, the organism is no longer able to maintain the higher energy state and death ensues.

Thus we can see the need for an energy conserving system. It is the purpose of later chapters in this book to examine how cells are structurally and chemically adapted to raise their lowest energy state, and to maintain this metastable state once acquired.

1.2   Uses of energy in cells

It has been stated that energy must be available in living systems to power the various processes associated with them. Table 1 summarizes the requirements for energy in cells.

Table 1

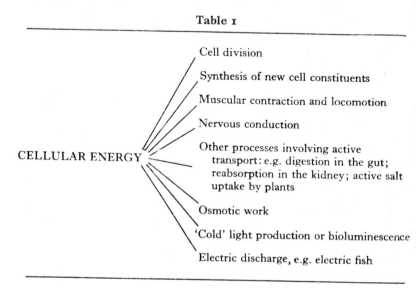

CELLULAR ENERGY

- Cell division
- Synthesis of new cell constituents
- Muscular contraction and locomotion
- Nervous conduction
- Other processes involving active transport: e.g. digestion in the gut; reabsorption in the kidney; active salt uptake by plants
- Osmotic work
- 'Cold' light production or bioluminescence
- Electric discharge, e.g. electric fish

1.3   What type of energy is most useful in cellular systems?

In order to answer this question, it is necessary to ask further questions about the 'usefulness' of forms of energy as they apply to living organisms, and then to consider the six major forms of energy in relation to them.

(1) Can it be TRANSFERRED easily?

> The form of energy must be transferable between cells and within cells so that it can be moved to any site within the organism as required.

(2) Can it be TRANSFORMED easily?

> The energy currency must be readily convertible into a variety of forms as demanded by those processes shown in Table 1.

(3) Can it be made AVAILABLE easily?

> Any living organism must be able to obtain its energy currency easily, or generate its own supply from precursors which may in the first instance be more readily available.

(4) Can it be STORED easily?

It is obviously desirable that energy should be stored and made available when required. This means that the form of energy must be compatible with the life of the organism, but must not be easily lost. The form of the energy too, must be relatively stable, yet capable of rapid release when required.

(5) Can it be USED by the organism?

The energy must be in such a form that its entry into living organisms is compatible with life, and the organism itself must be structurally adapted to harness the energy once it becomes available to the organism.

Table 2 shows how the six major forms of energy measure up to the five critical questions proposed above. An S denotes 'suitable', an X denotes 'unsuitable'.

Table 2

Forms of energy	Suitability in relation to questions 1–5 (§ 1.3)				
	1	2	3	4	5
Chemical	S	S	S	S	S
Light	S	S	S	X	S
Electrical	S	S	S	X	S
Mechanical	X	X	S	X	X
Heat	S	X	S	X	X
Sound	S	X	S	X	X

From Table 2, it can be seen that chemical energy is the most suitable form of energy for use by living cells. Chemical energy is also advantageous compared with most of the other forms, in that carefully controlled amounts of energy can be released accurately and economically.

Considering the other forms of energy for a moment, electrical energy could be quite useful apart from its inability to be stored in living systems, and where electrical energy is used, as in nervous conduction, it is generated chemically. Again, green plants have the structural adaptations necessary for trapping light, but almost immediately light energy is converted into chemical energy. Occasionally, this process is reversed, as in certain bioluminescent organisms, producing a 'cold' light. The chemical pathway involved, however, is not a reversal of photosynthesis.

Heat energy is common to most living and non-living systems, but is unsuitable for a number of reasons. Firstly, high temperatures (energy in the form of heat) are incompatible with living systems, since excessive heat denatures proteins, particularly enzymes. Secondly, heat is far too easily lost or dissipated, and hence is useless for storage purposes. There are similar objections which can be raised for both mechanical and sound as possible forms of energy in living systems. All things considered, it is now obvious why chemical energy has become the common energy source for living organisms.

1.4 ATP—a high energy compound

The energy currency of living cells is a chemical compound called adenosine triphosphate (ATP). As a chemical energy source it exhibits all the properties outlined in the last section. ATP consists of a nitrogenous base, adenine, linked to the five-carbon sugar, ribose. A string of three phosphate residues is attached to the sugar molecule.

ATP can be hydrolysed to adenosine disphosphate (ADP) and inorganic phosphate (P_i) according to the equation:

$$ATP + H_2O = ADP + P_i + 30 \text{ Kjoules}$$

Removal of the terminal phosphate residue from ATP thus releases 30 Kjoules of heat/mole. In contrast, glucose–6–phosphate hydrolysis releases only 13 Kjoules/mole. For this reason ATP has become known as a 'high-energy' phosphate and the formula for ATP is often written as

$$\text{Ad-Ribose-P} \sim P \sim P$$

It is unfortunate perhaps that the formula of ATP is written in this way, because the squiggle notation ($\sim$) earlier came to be regarded as a 'high energy bond'. This of course is a total misconception. The idea that energy can be stored in the squiggle bond (a covalent bond) is obviously nonsense because energy is always required to break covalent bonds. Although the alternative term 'high energy compound' can also be criticized, it is a convenient term which arises from the difficulty that biochemists have encountered in finding a concise terminology to explain the important role of ATP in the cell. The term 'high energy' as applied to ATP is however only relative, because there are some organic phosphates (e.g. phosphoenolpyruvate) which liberate more free energy than ATP on hydrolysis and, strictly speaking, ATP is only a 'high energy' compound when considered with the other reactants and products of hydrolysis. Bearing this criticism in mind, we still feel justified in looking upon ATP as a special energy 'currency', but emphasizing its important role in linked reactions where phosphate group transfers take place in cells.

The reason why ATP is a high-energy compound is not clear, but it is almost certainly a result of the distribution of charge within the molecule. One possible explanation is that ATP may ionize as follows:

$$\overset{\displaystyle O^-}{\underset{\displaystyle O^{\delta-}}{\overset{\displaystyle |}{\underset{\displaystyle \|}{-O-P^{\delta+}}}}}-\overset{\displaystyle O^-}{\underset{\displaystyle O^{\delta-}}{\overset{\displaystyle |}{\underset{\displaystyle \|}{O-P^{\delta+}}}}}-\overset{\displaystyle O^-}{\underset{\displaystyle O^{\delta-}}{\overset{\displaystyle |}{\underset{\displaystyle \|}{O-P^{\delta+}}}}}-O\text{-Ribose-Adenine}$$

If this were the case, the ATP molecule must contain more chemical energy in order to maintain the integrity of the molecule in the face of opposed positive and negative charges on the oxygen and phosphorus atoms respectively. The chemical energy released on hydrolysis of the terminal phosphate of ATP is therefore greater than the amount released from conventional organic phosphates, where such opposed charges are absent.

Although this explanation of how ATP is a 'high-energy' compound may not be accurate, it does emphasize the important fact that the 'high energy' is not contained in a single bond but is a function of the molecule as a whole.

As the hydrolysis of ATP into ADP and P_i releases so much energy, it follows that the synthesis of ATP from these components requires at least an equal amount of energy. Thus the biochemical processes and cellular structures involved in the elaboration of ATP are of great importance in a discussion of energy metabolism in living cells.

1.5   The sources of energy for living organisms

Living organisms obtain energy for the synthesis of ATP by breaking down organic compounds such as sugars, fats or amino acids. The organism's source of these compounds allows us to place it into one of two categories:

(i) Heterotrophic organisms (animals and non-green plants). These assimilate the organic energy sources from the breakdown products of other organisms—either living or dead.

(ii) Autotrophic organisms (green plants). These are able to manufacture their own organic energy sources from simple inorganic compounds.

Consequently the synthesis of organic from inorganic compounds which occurs in autotrophs is the starting point for the energy flow through the living world.

The majority of autotrophic organisms are photosynthetic. They use sunlight energy to drive the synthesis of sugars and amino acids from carbon dioxide, water, and simple nitrogenous compounds. However, some autotrophic bacteria (the chemosynthetic bacteria) do not need to trap light energy as they obtain the energy required for the synthesis of sugars and amino acids from the oxidation of inorganic substances such as ammonia, hydrogen, or sulphur. The biochemistry of chemosynthetic processes is poorly understood and as they occur only in certain species of bacteria, and as bacteria do not possess chloroplasts or mitochondria, we consider that they are outside the scope of this book.

Figure 1–1 summarizes the relationships between the biochemical processes of heterotrophs and autotrophs.

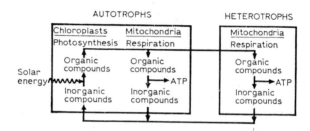

Fig. 1–1   Solar energy drives the synthesis of organic compounds from inorganic. The organic compounds may be broken down to inorganic in the mitochondria of autotrophs and heterotrophs. The energy released is used to drive ATP synthesis. Inorganic end products of respiration can be used in photosynthesis.

1.6   Cellular location of photosynthetic and respiratory processes

Photosynthesis takes place in subcellular organelles called chloroplasts. These are present in the green cells of autotrophic organisms (although the green colour may be masked by other pigments).

Respiration and the bulk of ATP synthesis occurs in the mitochondria which are present in almost all the living cells of both autotrophic and heterotrophic organisms. Notable exceptions are the bacteria, blue-green algae, and mammalian erythrocytes.

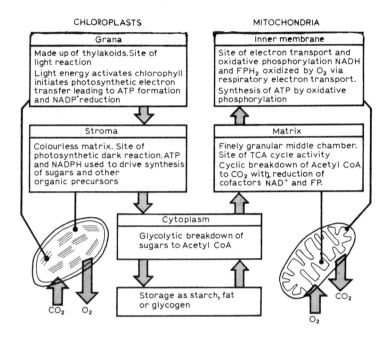

Fig. 1–2

Sunlight to ATP: The Flow of Energy 2

2.1 Introduction

The processes whereby living organisms transform light energy into chemical energy and make it available for ATP synthesis, can be conveniently divided into four phases.

The first two phases are what we normally refer to as photosynthesis and occur within the chloroplast. The *photosynthetic light reaction*, the capture of light energy and its conversion to chemical energy occurs in the grana (solid regions) of the chloroplasts and produces the co-factors necessary to drive the *photosynthetic dark reaction*. This 'reaction' which occurs in the chloroplast stroma (fluid region) is a cyclic series of reactions which converts simple inorganic substances into carbohydrates and other organic compounds. Carbohydrates are relatively stable and, with the exception of storage carbohydrates, relatively mobile compounds. They can therefore be translocated to other parts of the plant or they may become assimilated by animals. In both plants and animals the *breakdown of carbohydrates* and utilization of the energy for ATP synthesis begins in the cell cytoplasm (glycolysis) and continues in the matrix of the mitochondrion (TCA—tricarboxylic acid cycle). The synthesis of ATP (*oxidative phosphorylation*) occurs on the mitochondrial cristae (inner-membrane).

2.2 Oxidation–Reduction reactions—controlled release of energy

If you drop a match into the petrol tank of your car it will probably cause the car to move, but hardly in the direction you would like it to! If on the other hand, you treat your car in a more conventional manner and allow the petrol to be burned in successive small quantities you should have little trouble in moving the car in a controlled fashion. Similarly, in biological systems, energy is made available a little at a time to give maximum efficiency of ATP synthesis. Both the photosynthetic light reaction and oxidative phosphorylation processes involve organized series of oxidation–reduction reactions releasing energy at each step in the sequence.

Oxidation is always an energy-yielding process and can be considered to be the loss of an electron or electrons. For example oxidation of ferrous ions to ferric ions occurs by loss of a single electron.

$$Fe^{++} \longrightarrow Fe^{+++} + e^-$$

In another type of oxidation hydrogen ions (protons) may be given up as well as the electrons. An example of this is the oxidation of succinic acid to fumaric acid.

$$\begin{array}{ccc}
\text{COOH} & \text{COOH} & \\
| & | & \\
\text{CH}_2 & \text{CH} & \\
| \quad \longrightarrow & \| & \\
\text{CH}_2 & \text{CH} & +2\text{H}^+ +2\text{e}^- \\
| & | & \\
\text{COOH} & \text{COOH} & \\
\text{Succinic acid} & \text{Fumaric acid} &
\end{array}$$

Conversely reduction is always an energy-requiring process involving the gain of electrons (or electrons and protons). If the directions of the two oxidation reactions given above are reversed, then ferric ions may be reduced to ferrous ions by gaining a single electron, or fumaric acid may be reduced to succinic acid by gaining two protons and two electrons.

If one substance becomes oxidized, another must be reduced. The electrons released in the oxidation are used to bring about the reduction. The following is a general example involving two compounds A and B capable of oxidation–reduction (i.e. *electron carriers*):

$$A_{red} \longrightarrow A_{ox} + e^-$$

$$B_{ox} + e^- \longrightarrow B_{red}$$

(*red* and *ox* signify the reduced and oxidised states of the carriers respectively)

The electrons, however, will be passed directly from A to B. Therefore it is more meaningful to sum these two equations and eliminate e^-:

$$A_{red} + B_{ox} \longrightarrow A_{ox} + B_{red}$$

This equation can be rewritten as follows in a form which is more convenient for describing the series of oxidation–reduction reduction reactions used to control the release of the energy for ATP synthesis in biological processes.

$$\begin{array}{cc}
A_{red} & B_{ox} \\
& \diagdown \diagup \\
& \diagup \diagdown \\
A_{ox} & B_{red}
\end{array}$$

In biological oxidation–reduction systems the electron carriers are organized in such a way that the oxidation of a carrier releases more energy than is required to reduce the next carrier in the sequence. If there is a sufficient surplus of energy released at any stage this can be used to drive the synthesis of ATP from ADP and P_i.

There are four major classes of electron carriers involved in these energy conservation processes.

(i) *Pyridine nucleotides*

Nicotinamide adenine dinucleotide (NAD^+)* and nicotinamide adenine dinucleotide phosphate ($NADP^+$).*

These are electron and proton carriers undergoing oxidation–reduction in the following manner:

$$NAD^+ \text{ (oxidized form)} + H^+ + 2e^- = NADH \text{ (reduced form)}$$

$$NADP^+ \text{ (oxidized form)} + H^+ + 2e^- = NADPH \text{ (reduced form)}$$

(ii) *Flavoproteins*

These are enzymes with prosthetic groups derived from riboflavin (Vitamin B_2). The riboflavin derivative undergoes an oxidation–reduction involving protons and electrons.

$$FP \text{ (oxidized flavoprotein)} + 2H^+ + 2e^- = FPH_2 \text{ (reduced flavoprotein)}.$$

(iii) *Cytochromes*

These are also enzymes with prosthetic groups capable of oxidation–reduction. In this case the prosthetic groups are haem molecules, similar in structure to the haem of haemoglobin (see CHAPMAN, *Animal Body Fluids* in this series). The cytochromes are classified primarily on the basis of the precise structure of the haem part of the molecule, into cytochromes *a*, *b*, *c*, etc. Differences within each class in structure of the protein part of the enzymes are indicated by use of a subscript, e.g. cytochrome c_1, cytochrome a_3, etc.

The cytochromes of importance in biological energy conversion processes are cytochromes *a* and a_3, *b* and b_6, *c* and c_1, and *f*.

The cytochromes are electron carriers, the haem iron being capable of undergoing oxidation–reduction between ferric and ferrous forms. e.g.

$$\text{cyt } b \text{ Fe}^{+++} \text{ (oxidized cyt } b) + e^- \rightleftharpoons \text{cyt } b \text{ Fe}^{++} \text{ (reduced cyt } b)$$

(iv) *Ferredoxin*

A further electron carrier of importance in the photosynthetic system is ferredoxin, a protein containing iron which is not part of a haem residue. The iron can undergo oxidation–reduction in a similar manner to that of the cytochromes.

$$FD.Fe^{+++} \text{ (oxidized Ferredoxin)} + e^- \rightleftharpoons$$
$$FD.Fe^{++} \text{ (reduced Ferredoxin)}$$

2.3   Source of reducing power and electron transfer processes

Because of the overall passage of electrons along a series of oxidation–reduction carriers during the photosynthetic light reaction and oxidative

* Still referred to by some authors as DPN^+ and TPN^+.

phosphorylation, the processes are referred to as the photosynthetic electron transfer system, and the respiratory electron transfer system respectively. The precise sequence of electron carriers, particularly in photosynthesis, is not firmly established. The schemes we describe are the ones that we feel best fit the available experimental evidence. The initiation of electron transfer obviously requires the reduction of the first carrier in the series. In the photosynthetic electron transfer system, the first carrier to become reduced is ferredoxin. This is reduced by an energized chlorophyll electron. Chlorophyll can absorb visible light in the wavelength regions of 430 nanometres (violet) and 650 nm (red). If a photon (discrete unit) of light in these wavelength regions is absorbed, a chlorophyll electron is activated from its ground energy state to a higher energy state. The energized state of the chlorophyll electron is indicated in subsequent diagrams by an asterisk. Under normal circumstances the excited electron would fall back to its ground state, emitting the energy lost as heat or light (fluorescence). In the chloroplast, however, the energy may be trapped by using the excited electron to reduce ferredoxin.

In the respiratory electron transfer system the first carrier reduced is generally NAD^+. NAD^+ is reduced either by pyruvic acid or by one of the TCA cycle substrates, isocitric acid, α-ketoglutaric acid, or malic acid. Consequently, these reducing compounds become oxidized (see formulæ A).

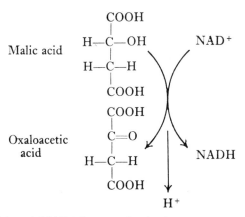

However, although NAD^+ is generally the first carrier reduced, there is one major exception. Succinic acid oxidation is coupled to the reduction of a flavoprotein (see formulæ B p. 12).

The first carrier in either system having been reduced, the linked sequences of oxidation–reduction reactions begin. The photosynthetic system is the more complex than the respiratory system as there are probably two separate electron transfer routes

(i) cyclic electron transfer—geared to the generation of ATP, and

COOH
|
H—C—H   FP
|
Succinic acid   H—C—H
|
COOH
                                          B
COOH
|
C—H
Fumaric acid   ‖
C—H   FPH$_2$
|
COOH

(ii) non-cyclic electron transfer geared to the production of NADPH and ATP.

NADPH and ATP are the two co-factors which are essential for driving the photosynthetic dark reaction. Figures 2–1 and 2–2 outline the reaction sequences of the cyclic and non-cyclic processes.

In the cyclic system oxidation–reduction reactions occur in an unbroken sequence as far as cytochrome f. The reduced cytochrome f is reoxidized by

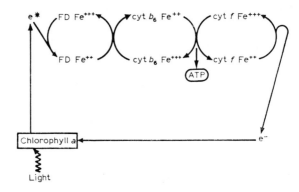

Fig. 2–1   Cyclic photosynthetic electron transport.

donating an electron back to chlorophyll. This electron will enter the ground state, ready for a further activation by a photon of light. There is at least one point in the cycle where sufficient energy is released to drive ATP synthesis—this, as shown in Fig. 2–1, is between cyt b_6 and cyt f.

As will be observed from Fig. 2–2 the non-cyclic system is somewhat more complex. This is because the system has a dual role, i.e. the reduction of NADP$^+$ to NADPH *and* ATP synthesis. The non-cyclic system is probably not physically divorced from the cyclic system. It is likely that

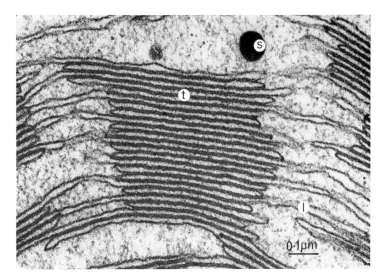

Plate 1 Section showing the arrangement of thylakoids to lamellae. (s) spherical (osmiophilic) granules; (l) lamellae; (t) thylakoids of granum. ×86 000 (os fixed). (Courtesy A. D. Greenwood)

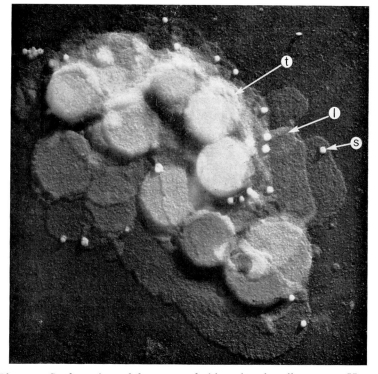

Plate 2 Surface view of fragment of chloroplast lamella system. Heavy metal shadowed. (l), (t) and (s) as for Plate 1. ×30 000. (Courtesy A. D. Greenwood)

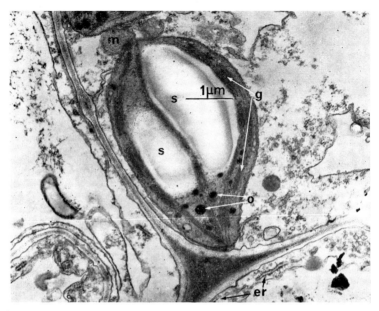

Plate 3 Whole Peperomia leaf chloroplast. (s) starch grains; (m) mito-chondria; (er) endoplasmic reticulum; (g) grana; (o) osmiophilic bodies. ×13 000. (Courtesy Dr. B. Juniper)

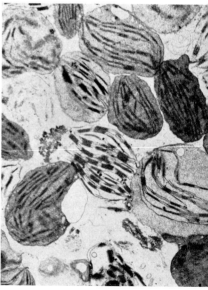

Plate 4 Washed isolated chloro-plasts of *Vicia faba* with outer mem-branes and stroma lost. Osmium fixed. ×4800. (Courtesy Dr. Rachel Leech and A. D. Greenwood)

Plate 5 Osmium fixed isolated chloroplasts from *Vicia faba* with membranes intact. ×6000. (Cour-tesy Dr. Rachel Leech and A. D. Greenwood)

the FD and cyt b_6 of Fig. 2–2 can react as shown for the cyclic system in Fig. 2–1. The two schemes are drawn separately merely for clarity. In the non-cyclic system the oxidation of reduced ferredoxin is used to drive the reduction of $NADP^+$. The hydrogen ions required for this process come from the splitting of water (photolysis). The hydroxyl ions remaining are

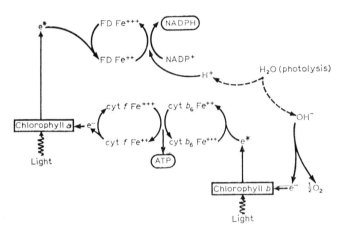

Fig. 2–2   Non-cyclic photosynthetic electron transport.

used to generate O_2 and electrons according to an equation which is slightly more complex than shown in Fig. 2–2.

$$4OH^- \longrightarrow 2H_2O + O_2 + 4e^-$$

This is the only source of oxygen evolved during photosynthesis. The electrons released in the process are passed to chlorophyll. This chlorophyll is probably chlorophyll b (different in structure from the chlorophyll a which is involved in the initial electron activation. The chlorophyll b electron can now be activated by a photon of light and used to reduce cyt b_6. The oxidation–reduction reactions completing the non-cyclic system follow the last part of the cyclic system i.e.

$$\text{Cyt } b_6 \longrightarrow \text{cyt } f \longrightarrow \text{chlorophyll } a$$

As in the cyclic system there is probably an ATP synthesizing site between cyt b_6 and cyt f.

Thus the overall result of photosynthetic electron transfer is (i) ATP production, (ii) $NADP^+$ reduction, and (iii) O_2 evolution. It is unlikely that the ATP and NADPH formed can be passed outside the chloroplast and so these can only be used to drive the synthesis of organic compounds from CO_2 in the dark reaction.

The mitochondrial respiratory electron transfer system has one major function—the synthesis of the ATP, necessary for driving the energy-requiring processes of organisms. As we have seen, the oxidation–reduction events are initiated by the reduction of NAD^+. The sequence of oxidation–reduction reactions involves NADH dehydrogenase (FP_N)—a flavoprotein enzyme, five cytochromes, b, c_1, c, a, and a_3, and finally oxygen. Cytochromes a and a_3 are usually written as cyt $(a+a_3)$ as, although there is evidence that these are separate entities, their physical separation has never been achieved. The reaction sequence is thought to be as follows:

$$
\begin{array}{c}
\text{ATP} \\
\uparrow
\end{array}
$$

TCA SUBSTRATE REDUCED $\quad NAD^+ \quad FP_NH_2 \quad$ cyt b Fe^{+++}

TCA SUBSTRATE OXIDIZED $\quad NADH \quad FP_N \quad$ cyt b Fe^{++}

$\qquad H^+ \qquad H^+ \qquad 2H^+$

ATP $\quad$ cyt c_1 Fe^{++} $\quad$ Cyt c Fe^{+++} $\quad$ ATP $\quad$ cyt $(a+a_3)$ Fe^{++} $\quad 2H^+$

cyt c_1 Fe^{+++} $\quad$ Cyt c Fe^{++} $\quad$ cyt $(a+a_3)$ Fe^{+++} $\quad \frac{1}{2}O_2$

$\quad H_2O$

The cyt $(a+a_3)$ complex differs from other cytochromes in that it is reoxidized by molecular oxygen. It is consequently often referred to as *cytochrome oxidase*. (See Chapter 3, § 3.6.)

Measurements of ATP synthesis suggest that there are three sites where ATP synthesis can occur in this sequence. These have been tentatively located (i) between NAD^+ and FP_N, (ii) between cyt b and c_1, and (iii) between cyt c and cyt $a+a_3$.

Succinic acid is oxidized by the flavoprotein enzyme succinic acid dehydrogenase (FP_s) which can then reduce cyt b. Subsequent oxidation–reduction reactions are shared with the NAD^+ linked systems.

$$
\begin{array}{c}
2H^+ \\
\uparrow
\end{array}
$$

Succinic acid $\quad FP_s \quad$ cyt b Fe^{++} $\quad$ Cyt c_1 Fe^{+++}

Fumaric acid $\quad FP_sH_2 \quad$ cyt b Fe^{+++} $\quad$ cyt c_1 Fe^{++} $\quad \longrightarrow O_2$

$\qquad\qquad$ ATP

It is apparent that this bypasses the first ATP synthesis site ($NAD^+ \rightarrow FP_N$) and it can be demonstrated experimentally that there are only two phosphorylation sites involved in the oxidation of succinic acid.

ATP synthesized within the mitochondria can be passed to the outside in exchange for exogenous ADP.

Table 3 summarizes the processes described in this section.

Table 3

Source of reducing power	Process	Products	Fate of products
Energized chloro-phyll electron	Cyclic photosyn-thetic electron transfer	ATP	Driving dark reaction
Energized chloro-phyll electron	Non-cyclic photo-syn. electron transfer	NADPH ATP	Driving dark reaction
T.C.A. cycle sub-strate	Respiratory electron transfer	ATP	Driving other energy requiring processes

2.4   The synthesis of ATP

We have seen that the energy liberated in the oxidation–reduction re-actions of electron-transfer can be used in ATP synthesis. However, nothing has been said so far about the mechanism of ATP synthesis. This is a problem which, despite intensive investigation during the last twenty years, has yet to be solved.

Although we cannot be absolutely certain that the phosphorylation mechanisms associated with photosynthetic and respiratory electron trans-fer are identical, the similarities in the organization of the two processes described and their similar dependences on the ordered structures of their respective organelles (Chapter 3) make it reasonable to assume that the processes must at least be conceptually similar. A good deal more research has been carried out into the mechanism of oxidative phosphorylation than that of photosynthetic phosphorylation. Consequently the discussion is largely one of the mechanism of oxidative phosphorylation. However, the problems encountered have been similar in both investigations and theories propounded to explain the process of mitochondrial ATP synthesis are equally applicable to the process of chloroplast ATP synthesis.

ATP synthesis is normally very tightly coupled to electron transfer. If a supply of ADP acting as a phosphate acceptor is not available to a mito-chondrial preparation, the rate of electron transfer is limited, even in the presence of adequate TCA cycle substrate. If ADP is added to mito-chondria, phosphorylation ensues concommittantly with an increased oxygen uptake. This is shown in Fig. 2–3. When all the ADP is converted to ATP (the point marked * in Fig. 2–3) oxygen uptake returns to the value observed prior to ADP addition. This phenomenon is termed respiratory control and is often used as a criterion of the quality of a mitochondrial preparation.

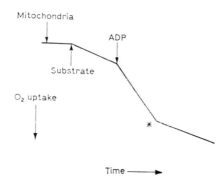

Fig. 2–3   Oxygen electrode tracing of oxygen uptake in mitochondria showing respiratory control. The oxygen electrode is an instrument used for measuring oxygen concentration in solutions. It works on the principle that the current passing between platinum and silver/silver chloride electrodes, set with a polarizing voltage of 0.6 V, is directly proportional to oxygen concentration. This diagram shows a recording of the decrease in current occurring as the dissolved oxygen is used up by the mitochondria.

Furthermore inhibitors of electron transfer (e.g. cyanide) also prevent ATP synthesis, and similarly substances which block the ATP synthetic mechanisms (e.g. the antibiotic oligomycin) prevent electron transfer. This strict coupling can also be seen in the action of certain chemicals which act as uncoupling agents e.g. 2,4-dinitrophenol and arsenate. Uncoupling agents allow electron transfer to occur at a maximal rate in the absence of any ATP synthesis. (See Fig. 2–4.) There is considerable evidence that ATP is not the first 'high-energy' compound formed during phosphorylation. The observation that some of the energy-requiring processes of mitochondria which are coupled to electron transfer (e.g. ion translocation) are not inhibited by oligomycin, suggests that a 'high-energy' intermediate of phosphorylation drives these processes. It is probable that this high-energy intermediate can, under normal circumstances, be used to drive ATP synthesis. It is possible therefore to divide the phosphorylation process into two phases:

(i) The generation of a 'high-energy' intermediate using the energy released in the oxidation–reduction processes.
(ii) The utilization of this intermediate to drive ATP synthesis.

The first process—*the Coupling process*—is where the greatest disagreement lies; there is some measure of agreement about the nature of the second process. The second process will be dealt with first. LEHNINGER (1958) put forward the idea that the known ability of a mitochondrial preparation to hydrolyse ATP into ADP and P_i (ATP-ase activity) represented a reversal of the normal enzymic processes of ATP synthesis. He further showed that

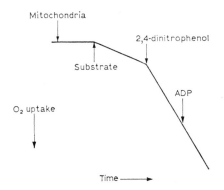

Fig. 2-4   Oxygen electrode tracing of oxygen uptake in mitochondria showing uncoupling by dinitrophenol.

their activity could be stimulated by dinitrophenol and inhibited by oligo-mycin which strongly supported his hypothesis. More recently, RACKER (1966) has shown that if all ATPase activity is removed from the mito-chondrial membrane, ATP synthesis cannot occur, but if a solubilized mitochondrial ATPase preparation (F_1) is added back to the membrane system (along with a number of other coupling factors) the ability to synthesize ATP is restored. (This work is discussed in greater detail in Chapter 3.)

The simplest scheme which can be proposed to explain these observa-tions would be as follows:

$$X \sim I + P_i + ADP \rightleftharpoons X + I + ATP$$

($X \sim I$ is the 'high-energy' intermediate of indeterminate structure formed during the coupling process.) It is probable, however, that this occurs in two stages:

$$X \sim I + P_i \rightleftharpoons X \sim P + I$$

$$X \sim P + ADP \rightleftharpoons X + ATP$$

The mechanism of formation of $X \sim I$ is in dispute. It was originally assumed that oxidation–reduction reactions of electron carriers led to the formation of a 'high-energy' form of those carriers involved at the site where ATP synthesis could occur, and that by a series of exchange reactions the high energy $X \sim I$ could be formed. This theory is referred to as the *chemical coupling theory* and many workers feel that this idea, although lacking in direct experimental proof, is the only one which adequately fits the available evidence. If the chemical hypothesis is correct it must be a multistep process, as the sites of arsenate and dinitrophenol uncoupling are known to be different. In the following scheme, which would fit much of the experimental data, dinitrophenol and arsenate are considered to uncouple by causing the dissipation of the 'high-energy' state, i.e. by stimulating the hydrolysis of $C_{red} \sim I$ and $X \sim I$ respectively.

$$C_{ox} + I \rightleftharpoons C_{ox}{-}I$$

$$C_{ox}{-}I + 2e^- \rightleftharpoons C_{red} \sim I$$

$$C_{red} \sim I + X \rightleftharpoons C_{red} + X \sim I$$

C is an electron carrier, which in its oxidized form reacts with an indeterminate compound 'I'. Reduction of $C_{ox}{-}I$ results in the formation of 'high-energy' $C_{red} \sim I$ and this can react with another indeterminate compound 'X' to form the 'high-energy' $X \sim I$.

The important feature of this theory is that at least some of the electron carriers must be involved in reactions other than oxidation–reduction, i.e. the formation of $C_{ox}{-}I$ and $C_{red} \sim I$. Consequently much effort has been put into searching for such compounds. Although GRIFFITHS (1963) found a phosphorylated derivative of NADH which stimulated ATP synthesis, and CHANCE (1966) observed the presence of an unusual cytochrome of the *b* type when the mitochondria were in certain energy states, it has been impossible to prove that these modified carriers are involved in the normal phosphorylation processes.

This lack of success led MITCHELL (1961) to propose an alternative scheme for coupling. *The Mitchell hypothesis*, or the *chemiosmotic hypothesis* as he has called it, suggests that the energy released during electron transfer is conserved in the form of a pH gradient across the mitochondrial inner membrane and that this pH gradient is used to drive the synthesis of $X \sim I$ from X—H and I—OH.

The basic tenets of the chemiosmotic hypothesis are that the inner membrane must be impermeable to protons, and that electron transfer results in an extrusion of protons from the mitochondria. Mitchell considers that this is achieved by virtue of the presence of both electron carriers, and proton and electron carriers in the electron transfer system. In addition the arrangement of the electron transfer system within the membrane is such that when coupled oxidation–reduction releases protons they move from the membrane in an outward direction. Conversely when protons are taken up they come from inside the mitochondrion. This idea is illustrated diagrammatically in Fig. 2–5.

Thus the net result of oxidation of TCA cycle substrate would be the transport of protons from the inside to the outside of the mitochondrion giving an increased proton concentration (increased acidity) outside the mitochondrion and a decreased proton concentration (increased alkalinity) inside.

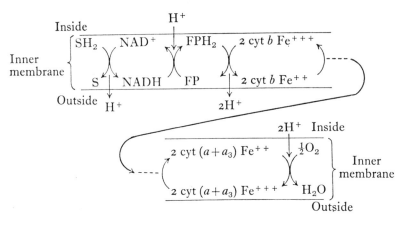

Fig. 2–5   Mitchell's scheme for proton extrusion during electron transport.

Mitchell has elaborated on his theory to show three positions of proton extrusion in the respiratory electron transfer system. These propositions bring his theory into line with the idea that there are three separate sites of energy conservation. In the modified theory, however, the order of electron carriers and the positions of phosphorylation sites do not correspond with the normally accepted ones.

The basic scheme for photosynthetic electron transfer (Figs. 2–1 and 2–2) involves only electron carriers and as such cannot be invoked as a proton translocating system as it stands. There is, however, good evidence that proton and electron carriers are also involved in photosynthetic electron transfer in the forms of a flavoprotein and plastoquinone, a substituted benzoquinone capable of oxidation–reduction between quinone and quinol forms. Mitchell considers that these are involved in a photosynthetic proton translocation process. In this case, however, electron transfer is believed to result in proton uptake rather than extrusion as seen in respiratory electron transfer.

Mitchell initially proposed that the proton concentration gradient established during electron transfer was used to cause a reversal of mitochondrial ATPase in the direction of ATP synthesis. Evidence that a high-energy intermediate ($X \sim I$) was formed prior to ATP synthesis caused him to modify his theory to account for the synthesis of $X \sim I$. Figure 2–6 is a simplified version of how Mitchell envisages the synthesis of $X \sim I$.

The enzyme involved would be $X \sim I$ hydrolase, an enzyme whose expected activity would be to hydrolyse $X \sim I$ to XH and IOH. This enzyme is postulated to be arranged anisotropically (i.e. directionally orientated) in the membrane so that protons are available only from the inside of the membrane and hydroxyl ions from the outside. Respiratory electron transfer as we have seen is considered to result in a proton excess outside the mitochondria and a deficit in the mitochondria. Fig. 2–6 (b) shows how the tendency of protons and hydroxyl ions to be drawn from the membrane as a result of the pH differential (represented by the circled ions) could be utilized to reverse the activity of $X \sim I$ hydrolase (Fig. 2–6(a)) in the direction of $X \sim I$ synthesis. As the direction of proton translocation in photosynthetic electron transfer is inwards the polarity of the chloroplast $X \sim I$ hydrolase would have to be opposite to that shown in the above schemes.

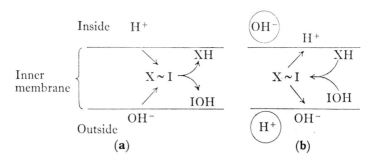

Fig. 2–6   Mitchell's scheme for $X \sim I$ synthesis in mitochondria.

Some of the objections to the chemiosmotic hypothesis have already been mentioned. Some of the experimental evidence supports the hypothesis, however. Mitchell has shown that electron transfer does result in proton translocation and JAGENDORF (1965) demonstrated that if the pH of the suspension medium of isolated chloroplasts is raised, ATP synthesis can occur in the absence of light. There is also evidence that some of the agents (e.g. dinitrophenol) which cause uncoupling of phosphorylation also increase the permeability of membranes to ions.

We imagine that the non-specialist might have difficulty in understanding the fundamental propositions of the chemiosmotic hypothesis. We hope that a summary of the main points of the hypothesis might help. These are that:

(i) The inner membrane of the mitochondrion is impermeable to hydrogen and hydroxyl ions.

(ii) Electron transfer from a proton and electron carrier to an electron carrier releases a proton (or protons) and conversely, electron transfer from an electron carrier to a proton and electron carrier takes up a proton (or protons).

(iii) The enzymes of the electron transport system are so arranged in the membrane that release of protons during electron transport occurs from the inner membrane in an outward direction and uptake occurs from inside the mitochondrion into the inner membrane. Thus the energy made available during electron transport is trapped as the potential energy of a proton concentration difference across the inner membrane.

(iv) The potential energy of the proton gradient is used to drive ATP synthesis.

2.5   The synthesis and breakdown of sugars

Now that the energy conversion processes occurring in chloroplasts and mitochondria have been dealt with, it remains to describe the metabolic pathways which link the photosynthetic and oxidative phosphorylation systems. These will not be described in detail as they are fully considered in another book in this series (BARKER—*Chemistry of the Cell*).

The NADPH and ATP which are produced during the light-driven phase of photosynthesis are used to drive the synthesis of sugars and other metabolites by the dark reaction. The dark reaction or 'carbon reduction cycle' is a complex metabolic cycle involving 3, 4, 5, 6, and 7 carbon sugars and their phosphorylated derivatives. Some of the key reactions in this cycle (a simplified version of which is shown in Fig. 2–7), are reduction or phosphorylation reactions requiring an input of energy. This is provided by the NADPH and ATP generated in the light reaction.

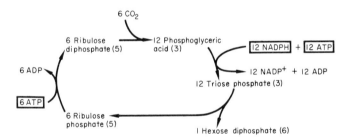

Fig. 2–7   Simplified version of 'carbon reduction cycle'. The figures in brackets represent the number of carbon atoms in each intermediate.

The important point to note is that the overall result of one turn of the cycle is the production of a molecule of hexose sugar (fructose or glucose) from six carbon dioxide molecules. The carbon reduction cycle, which was elucidated by Calvin and his co-workers by sophisticated chromatographic and radioactive tracer techniques, is, of course, considerably more complicated than shown here—the overall synthesis of sugar from CO_2 is, nevertheless, identical. More recent investigations have shown that, using modifications of this cycle, the NADPH and ATP generated in the light phase can also be used to drive the synthesis of fats and amino-acids from simple organic precursors.

If sugars are now to be used as an energy source for oxidative phosphorylation, they must initially be partially broken down outside the mitochondria during *glycolysis*. The overall result of glycolysis is the splitting of a six carbon sugar into two molecules of pyruvic acid (a 'three carbon' acid). As this is an oxidative process, a certain amount of energy is released during

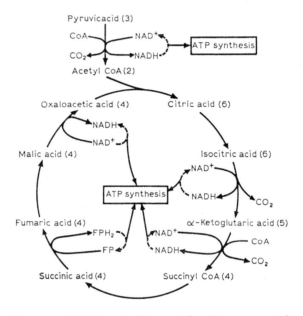

Fig. 2–8   Summary of TCA cycle. Figures in brackets represent the number of carbon atoms in each intermediate.

glycolysis, which can be made available for the synthesis of a small number of ATP molecules. The bulk of the energy for ATP synthesis, however, is released when pyruvic acid is further broken down in the mitochondria by the TCA cycle. This is summarized in Fig. 2–8.

Pyruvic acid becomes oxidized to an activated form of acetic acid known as acetyl CoA. This reaction involves the addition of a complex molecule known as Coenzyme A and the removal of CO_2 (decarboxylation). The oxidation is coupled to the reduction of NAD^+ to NADH. The acetyl CoA now undergoes condensation with oxaloacetic acid to give citric acid. In the course of a single turn of the TCA cycle, the citric acid is broken down by a series of oxidation and decarboxylation reactions to regenerate more oxaloacetic acid. At three points in the cycle NAD^+ is reduced to NADH and in the oxidation of succinic acid, flavoprotein becomes reduced. The reoxidation of these electron carriers initiates the oxidation–reduction processes of electron transport which, as we have seen, leads to ATP synthesis. It is very important to remember this connection between the TCA cycle and the electron transport and oxidative phosphorylation systems.

Structural Design of Chloroplasts and   3
Mitochondria

3.1   Molecular complexity demands an orderly structure

If the complex biochemical activity taking place in chloroplasts and mitochondria, reviewed in the previous chapter, is to have any real meaning, it
must be related to an orderly structure. For a multienzyme system to
control the release of energy along well-defined electrochemical gradients,
so that energy-rich molecules are synthesized, a high degree of spatial and
temporal organization is necessary. It is the purpose of this chapter to review the evidence relating the structural design of chloroplasts and mitochondria to their functions.

3.2   The particulate nature of the organelle membranes—a clue to the problem?

In attempting to answer such questions as 'how are the enzymes arranged?'—'are the component parts sequentially arranged and rigidly
positioned?'—'how is electron flow maintained if the components are
fairly rigidly positioned?' etc., it is important to look at the structure and
properties of organelle membranes. The improvements in electron microscopic techniques in this respect have been of paramount importance. Although the boundary membranes of chloroplasts and mitochondria appear
to conform basically to the 'unit membrane' structure (ROBERTSON 1962,
1964), they are unusual in two senses. Unlike the cell membrane, both
chloroplasts and mitochondria possess a double membrane and secondly,
in both organelles the electron microscope reveals a particulate structure
for the inner membranes. For example on the one hand there appear to be
complex particles in the chlorophyll-bearing lamellae of chloroplasts, (see
§ 3.4) and on the other the complex sheets of stalked particles on the cristae
of mitochondria. (See § 3.6.) However, all of these observations and deductions depend upon particular methods of chemical treatment and fixation.
When for example, permanganate fixation is used instead of osmium fixation, distinct differences in the appearance of membranes are apparent.
Care must therefore be exercised in the interpretation of all electron
micrographs because of the possibility of fixation artefacts.

Indeed, before we discuss the size and structure of chloroplasts or mitochondria, the following points should be borne in mind, since one, or any
combination, of these factors has an important bearing on the interpretation of apparent size, shape, and conformation of these organelles.

(i) The methods used to fix and stain the materials.

(ii) The time and point at which the materials were fixed (important when considering conformational changes).

(iii) The type of cell from which the organelle originated.

(iv) Whether the organelles were *in situ* or *in vitro*.

(v) The nature of the optical system used in observing the organelles.

Bearing these points in mind, the structures described below are based on a consensus of present day opinion, although many of the ideas are still highly speculative and much disagreement exists between scientists.

3.3 The occurrence and structure of chloroplasts

With the exception of bacteria and the blue-green algae, photosynthesis is carried out by organelles known as chloroplasts. Chloroplasts are members of a group of plant cell organelles collectively known as 'plastids'. Chloroplasts, however, are the most extensively studied of the plastids because of their association with photosynthesis, their colour and their

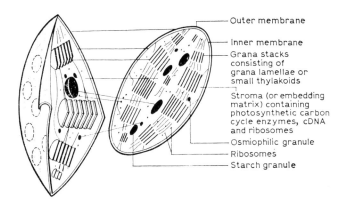

Fig. 3–1   (Redrawn partly after Dr. D. von Wettstein, Institute of Genetics, Copenhagen.)

prominent size. Most chloroplasts in higher plants for example are ellipsoidal or lens-shaped, ranging in long diameter from 4 to 10 μm. In certain algae they may even be larger. Chloroplasts, as their name suggests, are found only in the green cells of plants and especially the leaves, where they are exceedingly numerous in the palisade and mesophyll tissues. Chloroplasts are never found in meristematic tissues.

As shown in Plate 1 and Fig. 3–1 the chloroplast is surrounded by a double membrane about 30 nm in total thickness.

The outer chloroplast membrane is similar to the plasma membrane and can be interpreted in terms of the bimolecular layer theory of membrane structure, i.e. the 'unit membrane' proposed by Robertson. The inner chloroplast membrane, however, is very intricately elaborated to form a system of leaves or lamellae. It would appear, as with the mitochondrion, that the outer membrane is a derivative of the parent cell, isolating the organelle from the surrounding cytoplasm, whereas the inner membrane serves to contain the chloroplast (or mitochondrial) material. (See Chapter 5 on the possible role of chloroplast and mitochondrial DNA).

The inner portion of the chloroplast is clearly divisible under both light and electron microscopy into two parts. (i) The embedding, colourless STROMA, and (ii) the membrane system made up of closed flattened sacs referred to as THYLAKOIDS (meaning 'sac-like'). The thylakoids are closely

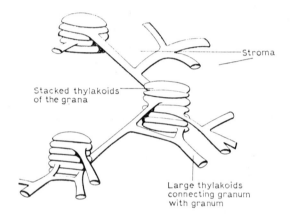

Stroma

Stacked thylakoids of the grana

Large thylakoids connecting granum with granum

Fig. 3–2   Three-dimensional model showing one interpretation of the interconnections between grana.

packed into certain areas, like piles of almost circular leaves; such areas are referred to as GRANA. There may be as many as 40 to 60 grana per chloroplast, and anything from 2 to 100 thylakoids per granum. In addition thylakoids also extend in a less stacked form (large thylakoids) throughout the stroma, linking one granum with another (Plates 1 and 2). The three dimensional linking plan is of course complex, although a number of models have been proposed which attempt to explain the systems (see Fig. 3–2). Thylakoids can assume a variety of configurations: some are widely separated as in the red algae, others are intimately packed together as in most of the higher plants. All chloroplasts are capable of quantum conversion, but the significance of the various thylakoid configurations is as yet unknown.

Other conspicuous features of most chloroplasts are (i) the starch grains—Plate 3—(absent when the plant has been kept in the dark for 24 hours), and (ii) the osmiophilic granules in the stroma. The function of the osmiophilic granules is not understood.

Most of the structures described here are those typically seen in higher plants. In conclusion we should state that the chloroplasts of the algae are basically similar in pattern, and there is evidence to suggest that the differences between higher plants and the various algae represent an evolutionary progression in chloroplast complexity (GREENWOOD 1969).

3.4   Correlation between structure and biochemical function—chloroplasts

The isolation of pure, undamaged chloroplasts has not proved easy (see Chapter 4). Consequently, although the association between chloroplasts and photosynthesis has been known for some considerable time, the absolute number of functions carried out by chloroplasts is still in doubt. In 1957 Arnon and co-workers established that the intact chloroplast was indeed the photosynthetic unit. Today this concept is basically true, although recent experimental evidence (WHITTINGHAM 1969) suggests that some processes in the dark reaction (e.g. sucrose synthesis) may possibly take place outside the chloroplast. One of the real difficulties has been that chloroplasts are frequently leaky after isolation, or very soon become so on standing. Indeed, electron microscopy on chloroplast suspensions reveals in most cases that the chloroplasts have lost the outer membrane and appear as in Plate 4. It is obvious that harsh isolation treatment rapidly damages the outer membrane and leads to a loss of soluble contents from the inside. However, if plant leaves are macerated gently, followed by shorter centrifugation times, intact chloroplasts are obtained but the yield is low, Plate 5. With these difficulties in mind let us return to the problems of structure and function.

In most plant cells, the thylakoid membrane contains the chlorophyll and the quantum conversion apparatus. The thylakoid is also the site of oxygen evolution and photophosphorylation. Examination by Park of the fine structure of the thylakoid using heavy metal shadowing in 1961, showed it to be composed of particulate units, which were called quantasomes. Park originally interpreted these structures as the primary photosynthetic units. In section these units appear more or less rectangular, but have a three-dimensional structure, being about 18 nm long, 15 nm wide, and 10 nm thick. Each unit appears to be composed of four subunits which are estimated to be 6–9 nm in diameter. Examination by freeze-etching (see Plate 6) also reveals particulate units in the thylakoid membrane. However, there is a further complication in that the particles just described are grouped rather characteristically on the outer side of the thylakoid membrane, whereas on the inside surface of the thylakoid there appear to be ungrouped particles 6 nm in diameter (Fig. 3–3).

Since Park's findings and his interpretation of the quantasome in 1961,

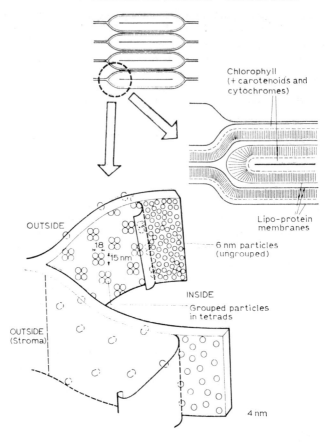

Fig. 3–3   Hypothetical models showing: (i) the thylakoids of a granum, and the possible arrangement of chlorophylls in relation to lipo-protein membranes (redrawn after Hodge); (ii) A portion of thylakoid membrane (angled) with inside and outside surfaces folded back to reveal the various arrangement of particles on and within the membrane (based on models proposed by Dr. Park and Dr. Branton). Plate 6 is an oblique fracture across several thylakoid membranes. The association of specific particles with specific photosynthetic molecules is still highly speculative, as are the arrangements of the particles themselves. For other interpretations see HALL & RAO—*Photosynthesis* in this series.

serious doubts have been expressed as to whether quantasomes do in fact represent the basic photosynthetic unit. Despite these doubts, most investigators agree that there is a particulate subunit within the thylakoid membrane, but as NORTHCOTE (1968) has said 'it is difficult to ascertain whether the membrane is actually composed of a repeating basic unit or

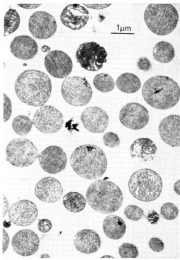

Plate 6 Freeze-etched thylakoid membrane showing the arrangement of particles at various membrane surfaces. (t) thylakoid membranes; (p) various particulate membranes of the thylakoid. ×100 000. (Courtesy Dr. D. Branton)

Plate 7 Isolated blowfly muscle mitochondria from 2-day-old flies. ×13 000 (Glut/Os). (Courtesy Dr. M. Tribe and Dr. D. Ashhurst)

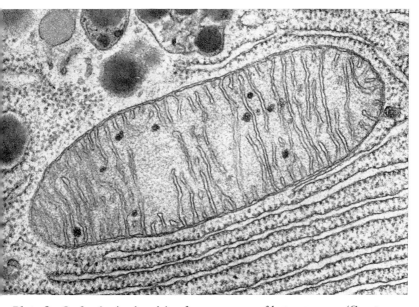

Plate 8 Os fixed mitochondrion from pancreas of bat. ×73 000. (Courtesy Professor K. Porter)

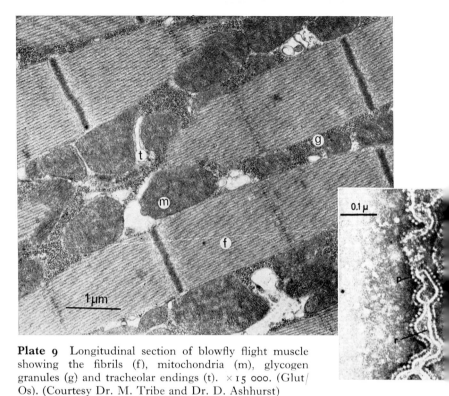

Plate 9 Longitudinal section of blowfly flight muscle showing the fibrils (f), mitochondria (m), glycogen granules (g) and tracheolar endings (t). ×15 000. (Glut/ Os). (Courtesy Dr. M. Tribe and Dr. D. Ashhurst)

Plate 10 (*inset*) Ribbon (r) of stalked particles (p) from blowfly mitochondria. ×133 000. (Neg. stain). (Courtesy Dr. E. Munn)

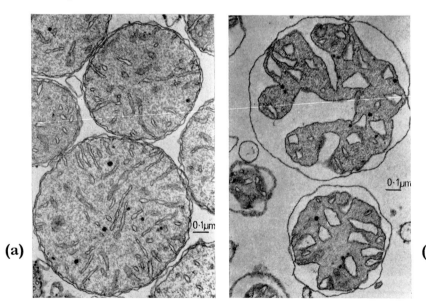

(a)

Plate 11 Osmium fixed isolated mitochondria from mouse liver. (**a**) orthodox configuration, (**b**) contracted configuration. ×66 000. (Courtesy Dr. C. Hackenbrock)

whether the particulate units are superimposed upon or embedded within a matrix, and moreover whether this matrix is further composed of repeating subunits'. According to Park and co-workers, the particles or quantasomes are composed of approximately 50 per cent protein and 50 per cent lipid, and carry chlorophylls, carotenoids, cytochromes, and other co-factors. The arrangement of the various molecules is highly speculative and it has been suggested that the quantasome unit might be the primary photo-synthetic unit, as predicted from theoretical kinetic studies. There is how-ever, little evidence to support this idea. Whatever the outcome, it is cer-tain that the arrangement of chlorophylls and other important molecules is highly ordered within the thylakoids.

The location of enzymes responsible for fixing carbon dioxide into sugar is the chloroplast matrix or stroma. In addition to these enzymes, which are presumably located close to the sites of photophosphorylation, the stroma also contains chloroplast DNA, ribosomes, and indeed a complete system for protein synthesis.

3.5   The occurrence and structure of mitochondria

Extensive studies have shown that mitochondria are present in the living cells of all organisms with the exception of bacteria and the blue-green algae. This fact may be of significance in relation to the possible evolu-tionary origin of mitochondria (Chapter 5). In addition certain highly specialized cells such as mammalian erythrocytes, have lost their mito-chondria as a secondary feature.

In situ, mitochondria (the name means 'thread-granule') are extremely variable in shape, ranging from spherical to very elongate and even cup-shaped, a feature which is accentuated by their plasticity. *In vitro* both isotonic and hypertonic media tend to preserve the natural state (i.e. *in situ*) rather better than hypotonic solutions, which make mitochondria swell and assume a more spherical shape. Again, when considering size there is much variation. For example, rat liver mitochondria are usually sausage-shaped, being about 1.5 μm in their major axis and 0.5 μm in their minor axis, with maxima of about 3 μm and minima about 0.25 μm. In other cells, especially those which are metabolically less active, mito-chondria may be considerably smaller and fewer in number, whereas in very active cells such as flight muscle fibres, or kidney convoluted tubule cells, or pancreatic cells, mitochondria may be up to 10 μm in length, and exceedingly numerous.

Figure 3–4 shows a histogram distribution of blowfly flight muscle mito-chondria isolated from 2 day adult flies, to show the size distribution en-countered in a particular tissue. An electron micrograph of a pellet of these mitochondria is shown in Plate 7.

Figure 3–5(a) and Plate 8 show a fairly typical animal cell mitochond-rion. Figure 3–5(b) shows a more typical plant cell mitochondrion.

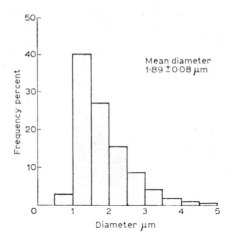

Fig. 3-4 Size distribution of isolated mitochondria from two-day-old blow-flies based on Coulter counter and electron micrograph analyses. (Data after Tribe and Ashhurst.)

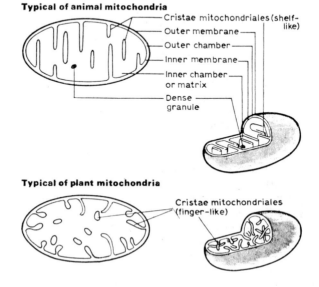

Fig. 3-5 (Based on models by Prof. A. Lehninger.)

As can be seen, the mitochondrion possesses a double membrane. Each membrane in turn encloses a chamber, in such a way that the two chambers do not appear to communicate with each other.

The outer membrane is comparatively smooth, whereas the inner membrane is extensively infolded. These infoldings were referred to originally by PALADE (1956) as *cristae mitochondriales*. In animal cells the cristae are usually pronounced and bold, whereas in plant cells they are usually more delicate and finger-like. However, cristae are very variable in their infolding; some extend right across the short axis, some only partially; in some mitochondria they are widely spaced, in others they are closely packed. Usually cristae lie transverse to the long axis, but occasionally they are orientated obliquely or even longitudinally. Again, mitochondria from very active cells have highly complex and closely packed cristae (Plate 9). In metabolically less active cells, cristae are fewer and less strongly infolded.

The inner chamber contains the matrix of the mitochondrion. In some cases, the matrix is continuous throughout the inner chamber, in others it is not, and in still others there are fenestrations which presumably facilitate transport between adjacent cristae and hence within the matrix. The matrix itself has significant electron density and is finely granular. The matrix is known to contain considerable protein, some lipid, and traces of nucleic acids. The organization of the matrix is probably semi-rigid, rather than a dilute fluid. To propose this arrangement makes more sense if, as seems likely, certain enzyme complexes are located here. In many mitochondria, especially those fixed with osmium tetroxide, electron dense particles (approximately 25 nm in diameter) also occur in the matrix. These particles undergo changes in number, position, and electron opacity, depending upon the metabolic state of the mitochondrion. It seems likely that these dense granules are sites of cation accumulation (e.g. Ca^{++}), since the complex movements of ions in and out of mitochondria are known to be of considerable importance in mitochondrial metabolism.

Closer examination of the inner cristal membrane after osmium fixation (but not permanganate fixation) followed by negative staining,* reveals the presence of numerous regularly repeating units, often referred to as stalked particles or Férnandez-Moran particles, after their discoverer in 1962. (Plate 10.)

In beef heart mitochondria at least, there are estimated to be some 4000 stalked particles per μm^2. A few years ago, considerable controversy existed about the possibility that these stalked particles were artefacts of negative staining. However, their reproducibility from many different mitochondrial sources, their regular arrangement, and more recently, the specific biochemical functions attributed to them, would indicate that they are indeed real structures. However, there is still doubt as to whether or not the particles protrude from the membrane in the natural state, or whether they

---

* See GRIMSTONE—*The Electron Microscope in Biology.*

are normally smaller and obscured by other proteins. Stalked particles are in fact most visible after mitochondria have been swollen to disrupt them, and then subjected to negative staining. It appears that the surface tension forces on drying the negatively stained preparation break open the mitochondrion, thus enhancing the appearance of these particles. The size of stalked particles as shown in electron micrographs too in some cases presents problems. If the measurements as viewed (see Fig. 3–6) are the actual *in situ* measurements, it is difficult to see how they fit together in mitochondria with closely packed cristae.

Another objection is that freeze-etched (BRANTON 1969) and freeze-fractured mitochondria (BULLIVANT 1970), which perhaps preserve the appearance of cell inclusions more faithfully (see A. V. GRIMSTONE, Studies in Biology No. 9), do not show the presence of stalked particles. The micrographs do, however, reveal a particulate structure for the inner membrane and cristae.

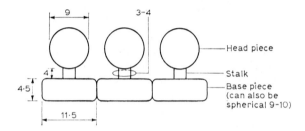

Fig. 3–6   Stalked particles or tripartite repeating unit.

With these objections in mind, we can state that three parts can be recognized in negative stained preparations of cristal membranes. They are a head piece, a stalk, and a base piece; hence tripartite repeating unit; the measurements are given in nm units in Fig. 3–6.

In contrast, less is known about the fine structure of the outer membrane, although there is some evidence both from negative stained and freeze-etched preparations to suggest that it too is particulate, and that a monopartite repeating unit may be present. Earlier suggestions that the outer membrane had stalked particles on its surface are unfounded and these, if present, were probably the result of contamination from inner membrane units after disruption of the mitochondrion. Like the inner membrane, the outer membrane consists of phospholipid and protein, but unlike the inner membrane, the outer membrane has a higher lipid content and a lower protein content. In this respect the outer membrane appears to resemble more closely the 'unit membrane' structure than the inner membrane, which appears to be thicker in some electron micrographs, where osmium fixation has been used.

3.6 Correlation between structure and biochemical function—mitochondria

It has already been stated that questions concerning the sequential and positional effects of enzyme components might be answered by looking at the unique arrangement of chloroplast and mitochondrial membranes.

One question which immediately springs to mind, is the significance of the cristae in mitochondrial structure. In answer to this question we might postulate that either the complex cristae infoldings provide access to certain respiratory enzymes present in the matrix, or that the cristae provide additional membrane surface to accommodate certain enzymes, or both.

Mitochondria, as we have seen, carry out a number of functions, which are primarily geared to the production of ATP. Consequently, the number of enzymic reactions involved is probably in excess of 100, and may be conveniently summarized as follows:

(i) enzymes of the tricarboxylic acid cycle;
(ii) enzymes involved in fatty acid oxidation;
(iii) enzymes involved in electron transport and ATP production;
(iv) enzymes involved in translocation, especially of ions and adenine nucleotides;
(v) enzymes involved in protein and lipid synthesis.

From a functional point of view, the physical state, or manner of binding of the respiratory chain components into the membrane system is the key to the organizational problem. In other words, there must be some regularly occurring pattern of groups of enzymes in, or bound to, mitochondrial membranes.

It was with this idea in mind that research workers in the early sixties began to look for organized groups of membrane-bound enzymes, or *enzyme complexes* within mitochondria. The rationale behind their approach was that the chemical entity of the mitochondrion was capable of stepwise disassembly and reassembly from 'component units' or particulate membrane fractions. These fractions can be obtained in a number of ways;

(i) by controlled swelling in water which brings about mechanical disruption followed by
(ii) sonication and differential centrifugation, and/or
(iii) detergent action with such agents as deoxycholate or digitonin.

By further sophisticated biochemical techniques, it has been possible to identify two major groups of enzyme complexes.

1. The primary DEHYDROGENASE enzyme complexes, i.e. those associated with the tricarboxylic acid cycle (with the exception of succinic dehydrogenase and NADH dehydrogenase), and therefore responsible for initiating electron transfer.

2. The enzyme complexes I, II, III, and IV associated with the components of the respiratory chain.

The link between the two main groups of complexes is membrane-bound NAD.

In identifying these complexes, the problem of damage or disruption of the organelle should be borne in mind, since it may alter the position of certain components within the complexes. However, some measure of the damage can be obtained by reassembling the complexes and measuring the

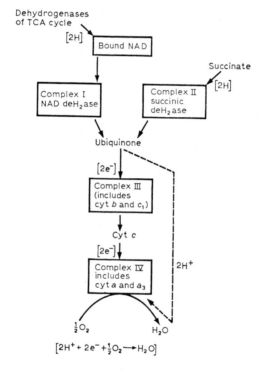

Fig. 3–7

activity against the original particle. Remarkably, reassembly is possible, although the activity is usually diminished to some extent because of the loss of certain components which are not fixed structurally into the lipoprotein network. In addition, reconstituted complexes are incapable of phosphorylation.

The overall relationships between the enzyme complexes are given in Fig. 3–7.

In 1952, PALADE proposed that the probable site of the respiratory chain was the inner mitochondrial membrane. Many research workers subsequently adopted his proposal as a starting point for their own research. In 1957, Lehninger suggested that the respiratory chain was an integral part of the inner membrane, but rather than being part of the basic monolayer ('unit membrane'), the assemblies were attached laterally. This arrangement in fact would satisfy two pieces of experimental evidence, (i) Sjöstrand's finding that the cristae membranes were somewhat thicker than the outer membrane, and (ii) that simple orientation of active sites of the component enzymes with respect to the plane of the membrane could be achieved. Such a scheme would incorporate Mitchell's idea of anisotropic enzymes (p. 20, Section 2.4) (i.e. enzymes specifically orientated to receive substrate from a given direction), and would also be consistent with experimental results showing directional properties of ion transport, and mechanochemical events in the membrane which are responsible for swelling and contraction cycles.

This model together with the evidence from the isolation of enzyme complexes, provides the basis for thinking that the respiratory assemblies occur in regularly repeating patterns.

With the discovery of stalked particles in 1962 therefore, it was not unnatural to think that these structures might represent the fundamental units of the electron transport chain.

However, this is now known to be an oversimplification of the situation. From the work of Racker and his co-workers, it is now generally accepted that the head pieces of the stalked particles (inner membrane subunits) are associated with a coupling protein called F_1. Soluble coupling proteins (i.e. enzymes involved in ATP production) had been known for some time, but the problem of associating them with specific ultrastructure had remained unsolved.

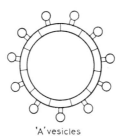

'A' vesicles

Fig. 3–8

The association between F_1 and the head piece came as a result of combined biochemical and electron microscope studies. By similar techniques to those outlined previously for the isolation of respiratory chain complexes, Racker's group obtained vesicles (called 'A' vesicles) with projecting subunits from the inner mitochondrial membrane (Fig. 3–8).

Biochemically, these structures can still perform the functions of electron transport, and indeed fairly extensive phosphorylation (ATP production). When such vesicles are chemically treated on a sephadex column (or alternatively with the enzyme trypsin), phosphorylation is lost and ATP-ase activity is stimulated (i.e. ATP is degraded). Structurally there is little change. When further treatment is given with urea both phosphorylating ability and ATP-ase activity are completely lost, although electron transport is maintained. Structurally the head pieces are removed from the vesicles (Fig. 3–9) (called SU vesicles 'S'—sephadex, 'U'—urea treated). The F_1 can in fact be purified, and when viewed under the electron microscope closely resembles the head pieces of stalked particles. To

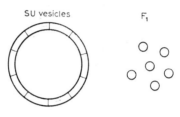

Fig. 3–9

complete the picture, when F_1 is added to SU vesicles the morphological structure of the original vesicle is restored. Biochemically, however, these reconstituted vesicles will perform electron transport but only very limited phosphorylation. For restoration of phosphorylation, other soluble coupling factors have to be added, although structurally they do not change the appearance of the vesicles.

From this simple account of a very elegant series of experiments, we know that the head piece (F_1) is a coupling enzyme when membrane-bound. Nevertheless, the chemical properties of F_1 can be altered in a number of ways; (i) by detaching it from the membrane and (ii) by subjecting the vesicles to trypsin or urea, when the removal of some inhibitor substance, frequently associated with the stalk (GREEN 1968) causes a complete reversal of the enzyme's activity. This is also known to be a feature of intact mitochondria. When mitochondria are carrying out their normal function, oxidation and phosphorylation are tightly coupled processes. When uncouplers (e.g. 2,4-dinitrophenol) are used, phosphorylation is lost and oxidation proceeds independently. However, if ATP is added to this system it is rapidly degraded by ATP-ase activity (i.e. by the reversible coupling protein F^1). The extent to which ATP-ase activity (normally latent) is carried out is frequently used as a measure of damage in mitochondria.

To summarize then (Fig. 3–10), the coupling protein F_1 is associated with the headpiece. The stalk may contain the inhibitor of ATP-ase activity and the base pieces are concerned with the complexes of the electron transport system.

Again, this model is probably too simple and perhaps a little misleading. Although there is good evidence that cytochrome c is located on the outer periphery of the inner membrane (i.e. the surface facing the outer membrane), the position of the other respiratory chain components is still debateable. Also, it is difficult to see how the F_1 headpiece functions if it actually projects into the mitochondrial matrix. Recent freeze cleavage studies (PACKER personal communication) indicate that F_1 is in fact normally 'tucked into' the membrane, where it is able to work in close apposition to the components of the electron transport system.

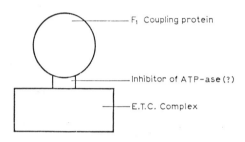

Fig. 3–10

As to the location of the dehydrogenases of the TCA cycle there is considerable controversy. There appear to be two reasons for this; (i) the more 'soluble' nature (i.e. on the basis of the isolation procedures used) of these enzyme complexes makes them more elusive compared with the respiratory chain complexes, and (ii) the different parameters and methods chosen by various research workers. In all cases work has centred around the isolation of the outer mitochondrial membrane from the inner membrane. With the exception of Green and his co-workers who have evidence that the TCA cycle dehydrogenases are associated with the outer membrane, the majority of workers favour their location within the matrix. It seems likely (although by no means established!) that they are loosely associated with the inner side of the inner mitochondrial membrane, rather than randomly floating in the matrix. Recent evidence which may add support to this idea comes from the freeze-etched preparations of liver mitochondria by WRIGGLESWORTH, PACKER, and BRANTON (1970). These workers found a fibrous network of protein in the matrix of contracted mitochondria (see § 3.7), which disappeared in orthodox or expanded mitochondria. The presence or absence of this network seems to be controlled by energy-dependent ion transport. These scientists propose that this evidence taken in conjunction with the very variable extractability of different mitochondrial enzymes, indicates that the matrix is not a simple solution of enzymes, but a highly organized series of components which differ in binding and association with the inner mitochondrial membrane.

3.7 Permeability and plasticity of chloroplasts and mitochondria

In our description of chloroplasts and mitochondria we have not been dealing with static structures within the cell, but rather with very vital and dynamic organelles. We have seen that they possess a double membrane, and it would be pertinent to ask why. There are probably three main reasons, which we have based on experimental evidence from mitochondria, although the principles apply equally to chloroplasts.

(i) The outer membrane forms a limiting boundary with the other elements of the cytoplasm. Certainly it is quite possible to remove the outer membrane from the inner membrane, and whereas the outer membrane is thought to be freely permeable to small molecules such as salts, sucrose, adenine nucleotides, and coenzyme A, it does not appear to be permeable to large molecules such as insulin or albumin. Also during metabolic activity the outer membrane does not appear to undergo any drastic conformational change, indicating that it plays a much more passive role compared with the inner mitochondrial membrane.

(ii) Between the outer and inner mitochondrial membranes there is a chamber which probably houses one or two enzymes which may be loosely associated with the outer wall of the inner membrane, and are thus afforded some protection by the outer membrane, e.g. adenylate kinase in liver mitochondria, and L-glycerol 3-phosphate flavoprotein oxidoreductase in blowfly flight muscle mitochondria.

Fig. 3–11   Digitonin-produced vesicles.

(iii) The inner membrane besides being more extensive in order to house the numerous respiratory assemblies, is also the site of selective permeability and translocation. Experimental evidence suggests that the majority of mitochondrial substrates must penetrate the inner mitochondrial membrane before they can be metabolized. Again, when considering ionic movements across membranes, the inner mitochondrial membrane is remarkably impermeable to even very small anions such as Cl^-. What is perhaps even more interesting is that digitonin-produced vesicles (i.e. where projecting subunits are pointing inwards, Fig. 3–11) also retain many of these properties. In general, however, the very complex behaviour of ions and other substances is beyond the scope of this book. One final point, however, requires mention with respect to the inner mitochondrial membrane and indeed to the chloroplast membrane as well. Since the ionic composition due to the presence of salts, nucleotides, proteins, and intermediates of metabolism, is constantly changing as a result of metabolic activity, there will be ionic fluxes between the inside and the outside of the organelle. Some of these changes will be passive, as we have pointed out, and some will be active, requiring the expenditure of energy. Since the balance of ions between the organelle and the surrounding medium influences the osmotic pressure as well, then cyclical fluxes of ions would be expected to lead to small amplitude swelling and contraction cycles in these organelles. This is precisely what has been found experimentally in both chloroplasts and mitochondria. In Plate 11a and b we can see when osmium is used as fixative there are quite marked differences in the conformational pattern of the inner mitochondrial membrane between resting (orthodox) and energized (contracted) states. Contraction can be brought about by the addition of ADP, by the hydrolysis of ATP, or by electron transfer. Alternatively, the contracted state can be dissipated and the orthodox state restored by the addition of ATP, by reverse electron transport, by uncoupling agents, by the translocation of divalent cations, and by ion-induced swelling. The changes brought about by these various agencies can also be observed from the changes in the light scattering properties of suspensions of these organelles.

4.1 Introduction

Some knowledge about the historical developments within any branch of science is necessary to place the present state of that science in perspective. The events which have led to our present understanding of chloroplasts and mitochondria (as summarized in Chapters 2 and 3) have followed and still are following many devious, yet interesting routes and this is an important feature of any major field of research.

4.2 Early landmarks

Today, it is all too easy to overlook some of the apparently simple problems and technical difficulties which confronted earlier scientists. One of the early problems was concerned with the growth of plants. Most people were aware that eating in animals was associated in some way with growth, and that breathing too was a vital process. There appeared to be no equivalent process in plants, and yet plants were still able to grow.

Investigations into this problem were made by a Dutchman, JAN BAPTISTA VAN HELMONT (1648), and an English cleric, STEPHEN HALES (1727). Van Helmont's experiments with willow shoots led him to believe that only water from the soil became transmuted into new plant material (wood). Largely due to improvements in light microscopy. Hales became interested in the structure of leaves, and particularly in the function of the fine pores (stomata). From his studies, Hales suggested that plants took in nourishment through these fine pores in addition to that which they obtained from the soil, and although he was unable to state exactly what was imbibed, his experiments did reveal that plants were able to change the composition of air.

Although hampered by phlogiston chemistry, Lavoisier and Priestley made major contributions to our present-day knowledge about the composition of air, and the complementary relationship between plant growth and respiration.

The discovery of oxygen independently by SCHEELE (1773) and PRIESTLEY (1774), triggered off a series of experiments of fundamental importance by LAVOISIER (1774) on the composition of air. Together with RUTHERFORD's discovery of nitrogen (1772) and BLACK's discovery of carbon dioxide (1777),* these experiments opened the way to an understanding of the factors involved in respiration and photosynthesis.

---

* Although the discoveries of the various gases are attributed to the scientists mentioned above, many of the present-day names of the gases were given at a later date.

In addition to his discovery of oxygen, Priestley's experiments on the 'purification of air' by plants are particularly relevant here. They are summarized in Fig. 4–1 below:

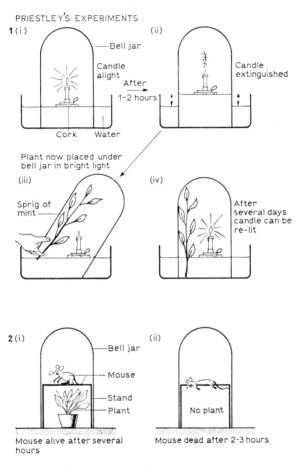

Fig. 4–1   Priestley's experiments.

The experiments are of immense interest as Priestley concluded that plants 'reverse the effects of breathing'. However, when they were repeated later by Priestley and others, they proved very fickle, and failure to repeat the original result may have been attributed to the size of the plant used, or more probably the variability of sunlight. In fact the importance of sunlight in the process of photosynthesis was not appreciated until the experiments of INGEN-HOUSZ in 1779. Ingen-Housz made three very important discoveries.

Firstly, he noted that both green and non-green parts of plants expired 'impure air' (CO_2) in the shade or at night, and hence showed some similarity with animals.

Secondly, he demonstrated that green matter is necessary for plant growth, and that woody stems, fruits, roots, etc., without green matter *always* consumed oxygen. The discovery that plants also respired subsequently puzzled many plant physiologists. The problem was that early measurements for photosynthetic activity might have been true values, or alternatively values which represented the difference between an unknown rate of photosynthesis working in one direction, and an unknown rate of respiration working in the other. Only when chloroplasts were free from mitochondria could true photosynthetic values be obtained, and it was not until 1954 when Arnon *et al.* first demonstrated 'photosynthesis in isolated chloroplasts' that the thorny problem was solved.

Ingen-Housz's third discovery was that *light* was essential for plant growth, and also for the liberation of 'dephlogisticated air' (oxygen). The concept of light as an energy source capable of synthesizing chemical energy under appropriate conditions came much later with the studies of MAYER in 1845, although SENEBIER (1782) had earlier demonstrated that light rather than heat from the sun was the important factor.

The years which followed Ingen-Housz's experiments, up to the middle of the nineteenth century, were mainly concerned with the fascinating problem of oxygen production. With the suggestion by Senebier (1782) and subsequent demonstration by DE SAUSSURE (1804) that carbon dioxide was the 'something from air' involved in the production of new plant material, the following facts were known:

(i) *In animals and plants*

FOOD (including plant matter) + AIR $\longrightarrow$
WATER VAPOUR + 'FIXED AIR' or 'IMPURE AIR' (CO_2)

and,

(ii) *In the green parts of plants*

SOMETHING FROM AIR (CO_2) + WATER $\xrightarrow[\text{+ green colouring}]{\text{+ light}}$
PLANT MATTER + Dephlogisticated or 'PURE AIR' (O_2)

(N.B. Energy relationships were not appreciated, but De Saussure's quantitive experiments revealed that the gain in weight of a plant during photosynthesis, plus the oxygen evolved exceeded the weight of CO_2 consumed. Therefore he suggested that the difference was due to the uptake of water.)

For many years considerable controversy raged over the production of oxygen. BERTHOLLET (1748–1822) and his followers advocated that oxygen came from water molecules, and that carbon dioxide was 'fixed' by hydrogen from water. On the other hand, Senebier and his followers proposed that oxygen came from carbon dioxide molecules. The controversy was not resolved until the 1930s and 1940s by the experiments of VAN NIEL with photosynthetic sulphur bacteria (1931) which showed that the sulphur released came from hydrogen sulphide, and the isotopic labelling experiments of RUBEN *et al.* (1941) and VINOGRADOV and TIES (1941). In Ruben's experiments, water was labelled with radioactive O^{18}; the subsequent detection of the O^{18} by mass spectrometry showed it to be exclusively in the oxygen released and not in the carbohydrate produced, thus confirming Berthollet's and van Niel's earlier predictions.

However, Senebier did make one other very interesting observation, which was frequently overlooked during the 'oxygen controversy'. He showed that shredded bits of leaves as well as whole leaves could release oxygen when immersed in water and subjected to sunlight. This observation was a landmark in the history of chloroplast study because it indicated that photosynthesis is not necessarily performed by the leaf as a single organ, but rather, as we know today, by the chloroplasts within the leaf.

At this point, it seems appropriate to confine further events specifically to the advances in chloroplast and mitochondrial research.

4.3 The major hurdles

A hundred years or so ago, when biochemical and microscopic techniques were less sophisticated, it was only possible to see that the cytoplasm of cells contained a variety of granular elements and inclusions. Indeed a popular concept of the times, which prevailed until the 1920s, was that living protoplasm was a homogeneous colloidal system—comprising hydrogel and hydrosol—without microscopic differences. Any differences in structural detail were attributed to artefacts caused by denaturation of living matter. Today, we know that green plants synthesize complex organic molecules from light energy falling on organelles known as chloroplasts, and that all living organisms generate their energy for various physiological requirements from small granular or threadlike particles known as mitochondria. In the course of just over one hundred years, several major hurdles have been cleared, either completely or partially. They may be summarized as follows:

(i) The discrimination between cellular organelles and other cytoplasmic contents. Both improvements in microscopy and histology were important in this respect.

(ii) The establishment of the cellular function of chloroplasts and mitochondria.

(iii) The development of suitable techniques for breaking up cells and isolating pure fractions of cell organelles intact.

(iv) The elucidation of major biochemical pathways in cells.

(v). The establishment of the fine structure of organelles with the aid of the electron microscope.

(vi) The assignment of specific biochemical roles to specific structures.

4.4   The discovery of chloroplasts

The first person to record seeing chloroplasts was the seventeenth-century plant anatomist NEHEMIAH GREW, but it is likely that other eminent cytologists of the period also observed them.

Following Ingen-Housz's discovery that only the green parts of plants (i.e. those containing chloroplasts) could 'correct bad air', the nineteenth century saw some major advances towards an understanding of chloroplast structure and function. In 1837 for example, DUTROCHET recognized that the green pigment chlorophyll was necessary for photosynthesis, and in the same year VON MOHL observed starch grains within chloroplasts. This observation was confirmed by SACHS, who in 1862, showed that starch was the direct product of assimilation of carbon dioxide in sunlight. Also during the latter half of the nineteenth century, many excellent studies were made on chloroplast structure and inheritance. It was discovered (though not universally accepted) that the chloroplasts of higher plants contained grana (MEYER 1883 and SCHIMPER 1885). However, with the concept of protoplasm as a homogeneous colloid becoming increasingly popular, 'grana' were dismissed as artefacts caused by denaturing of protoplasm, and the rediscovery of grana by HEITZ did not in fact take place until some fifty years later in 1936. Again, although TSCHIRCH (1884) suggested the existence of a chloroplast membrane which 'prevented chloroplasts from coalescing', many scientists of the time considered the chloroplast membrane to be an optical illusion. Final demonstration of the existence of such a membrane, with selectively permeable properties, was not achieved until some fifty years later (GRANICK 1938).

With respect to function, the ingenious experiments of ENGELMANN (1882, 1883) were outstanding. First, Engelmann cleverly selected a cylindrical form of filamentous green alga (*Cladophora*) with very regular distribution of chlorophyll. Then by placing the specimen in a micro-spectrum of light with its longitudinal axis at right angles to the direction of the Fraunhofer lines, he was able to show that oxygen-sensitive bacteria present in the medium moved to, and then congregated at, the areas of maximum absorption (mainly the red band—660 nm Fig. 4–2). In another experiment, with the filamentous alga *Spirogyra*, Englemann showed that the motile bacteria congregated around an illuminated area of the chloroplast, but not around a similarly illuminated area of colourless cytoplasm. These experiments demonstrated two important facts. First, that different wavelengths of the spectrum vary with regard to their effectiveness on photosynthesis, and second that as oxygen-sensitive motile bacteria are attracted to the chloroplasts, these bodies are the sites of oxygen pro-

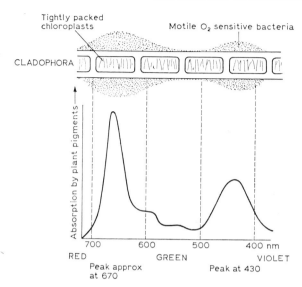

Fig. 4–2   Engelmann's experiments.

duction. Since the time of Engelmann, it has been generally accepted that the reaction sequence of photosynthesis begins and ends in the chloroplasts. Thus before the end of the nineteenth century, the existence and the essential function of the chloroplast, unlike mitochondria, was well established.

4.5   The discovery of mitochondria

It is difficult to attribute the discovery of mitochondria to any one person. However, KÖLLIKER (1850) was perhaps the first person to draw attention to the characteristically arranged granules in the sarcoplasm of striated muscle. These large mitochondria were later given the name sarcosomes by RETZIUS (1898), a name which is still used today specifically for the mitochondria of muscle tissue. The term 'mitochondrion', meaning 'thread-granule', was coined by Benda at about the same time, although the name was by no means universally accepted. In fact, no organelle has been given so many names!

Again, in 1888, it was Kölliker who first teased out the profuse, beadlike granules from insect flight muscle, and observed that they became swollen in water. He deduced quite correctly that the teased particles possessed a limiting membrane (compare similar deductions with chloroplasts).

With improvements in histochemical techniques and supravital staining (i.e. staining techniques with pieces of living material), it was eventually possible to demonstrate that mitochondria from a variety of different cells contained phospholipid and protein (REGAUD 1908). It was conceivable, therefore, that mitochondria had a distinct, although common structure, and perhaps a common function in different cell types. In this connection, the work of MICHAELIS (1898) with the dye Janus green B was most notable. Michaelis showed that certain components (mitochondria) within living cells could bring about an oxidation–reduction change in the dye Janus green B. The dye is used in low concentration made up in buffered saline. When pieces of fresh tissue are immersed in the dye, mitochondria stain bluish green, but as oxygen is consumed the dye is reduced to a pinkish colour and then finally to the colourless form. We now know that the mechanism involved is one in which the dye links with the flavoproteins of the electron transport chain, and it is possible to restore the blue colour on reoxidation due to the high cytochrome level in mitochondria. However, the full implications of Michaelis' observation were not appreciated until some ten years later, when KINGSBURY called attention to the possibility that mitochondria were the sites of cellular oxidation. In the intervening years, most theories relating to the function of mitochondria had favoured them in cellular differentiation, and as bearers of hereditary characteristics.

Following Kingsbury's suggestion in 1912, WARBURG (1913) found respiration to be associated with granular, insoluble elements of cell structure, which he recovered by filtration from tissue dispersions. Unfortunately, he failed at that time to connect them with mitochondria.

In 1914, work by LEWIS and LEWIS centred on observations into the number, size, orientation, and distribution of mitochondria in many different cell types. From such observations, mitochondria were soon recognized as important, universally occurring components of aerobic cells. It became particularly apparent that the numbers and activity of mitochondria reflected the cell's nutritional, metabolic, or endocrine state, and in consequence a respiratory function was finally established.

4.6   The isolation of intact organelles—an important step

For a detailed examination of the biochemical function of chloroplasts and mitochondria, it is necessary to isolate these organelles separately and intact. The only assumption is that the isolated organelles will behave in the same way as they do *in vivo*—perhaps at times a somewhat fallacious assumption! The advantages, however, are that it is possible to study an isolated system without interference from other cellular components, and the observed behaviour is attributed entirely to that organelle.

Historically, it is interesting that both HABERLANDT (1888) and EWART (1896) obtained 'isolated chloroplasts' by grinding leaves under water, which then liberated a small quantity of oxygen when exposed to light. However, the matter rested there until the late 1920s, when another early worker in this field, MOLISCH, took up the problem again (1925). Soon several biochemists became interested in the chemistry and functions associated with isolated chloroplasts, notably NOAK (1927), HILL (1937), MENKE (1938), and GRANICK (1938). Most of these workers obtained their chloroplast suspensions by grinding leaves with sand in osmotically compatible solutions, such as phosphate-buffered 10 per cent sucrose at a pH around 7. The chloroplasts once suspended were deposited by centrifugation.

At about the same time, similar techniques were being employed to try to isolate mitochondria. Prominent in this field were BENSLEY and his coworkers. Bensley's pioneering work on the isolation of mitochondria was continued and extended by the introduction of differential centrifugation by CLAUDE (1940) in his analysis on the composition of subcellular fractions. This work finally culminated in the first successful isolation of intact and apparently fully functional mitochondria by HOGEBOOM, SCHNEIDER, and PALADE in 1948.

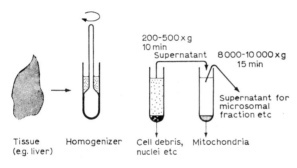

Fig. 4–3

Present day information about the biochemistry of chloroplasts and mitochondria is the result of perfecting the techniques of homogenization of cells and differential centrifugation; consequently it has been possible to localize different types of activity in different organelles. (An outline of these techniques is given in A. V. GRIMSTONE'S book—No. 9 in this series—page 43 and reproduced here, Fig. 4–3.) The initial problems facing early workers were immense, and it is perhaps worth while considering some of them here.

The problems fall under four main headings:

(i) *The selection of tissues*

As cells and tissues vary greatly in their activity, content, composition, fragility, density, and other properties, it is important to consider the specific problems associated with each cell or tissue type as they arise. For example, liver cells have been a major starting point for the isolation of mitochondria. However, liver is a very vascular tissue, and there are problems of contamination by erythrocytes when obtaining pure preparations of mitochondria. Even more troublesome is the problem of lysosomal contamination in a tissue which *in situ* has a high cell turnover rate. Lysosomes are of comparable size to mitochondria, and when damaged, release lytic enzymes which reduce mitochondrial activity.

(ii) *Problems of breaking the cell*

Disruption of cells is usually carried out mechanically, using one of the many types of homogenizer available. Disruption of cells may also be carried out by chemical methods or by ultrasonic treatment. The fragility of the tissue under consideration is usually the decisive factor in the choice of method to be employed. The cell biologist is striving to achieve minimal damage to the cell contents, whilst obtaining maximum purity and yield of the fraction under investigation. If valid observations are to be made, it is important that biochemical integrity is preserved, and microscopic examination (light or electron microscope) is often a desirable if not essential check.

(iii) *The selection of suspension media*

As water is the basis of life, the suspension medium employed for most experimental work is usually an aqueous solution of either (*a*) an organic acid (e.g. citric acid), or (*b*) sugar (e.g. sucrose), or (*c*) a saline (e.g. potassium chloride), although these have not precluded the use of non-aqueous solvents. The concentration of sugar or salt used in solution is usually chosen to be osmotically compatible with the tissue under investigation, the O.P. of the tissue fluid first being obtained by depression of the freezing point. The osmolarity of the suspension medium is important since hypotonic and indeed isotonic media cause swelling. On the other hand strongly hypertonic solutions cause some shrinkage and in addition reduce certain activities of the organelle in question.

In addition, the pH of the suspension medium must be akin to that which is found in the cell, since a change in pH can dramatically affect enzyme catalysed reactions.

The general tendency for organelles, such as chloroplasts and mitochondria to swell once isolated, can be prevented by the addition of certain divalent cations. Ca^{++}, however, is not usually employed, as it brings about uncoupling in mitochondria. Addition of other substances such as bovine serum albumin have proved useful in certain instances where long-chain fatty acids are released by mitochondria. The serum albumin is able to bind fatty acids, thus preventing their uncoupling action. Depending on the nature and origin of the organelles isolated, it is sometimes necessary to add certain co-factors such as cytochrome *c* in order to obtain 'best results', consequently although the basic suspension media are widely adopted, there is much mystique and superstition amongst research workers over the refinements necessary!

(iv) *The separation of fractions in suspension*

The technique which has been universally adopted for separating cell fractions is differential centrifugation. Recently, the process has been extended to the use of 'layering' and density gradient techniques.

In the centrifugation process, consideration must be given to:

(a) density and size of the required particles
(b) speed of spin
(c) time of spin
(d) temperature during the isolation process, and
(e) the effect of the isolation medium in which the particles are suspended (especially important in density gradient techniques).

In general, large particles need a lower speed to sediment them. However, time is a crucial factor with cell organelles as biochemical function is rapidly lost, although this may be delayed in most cases by maintaining the preparation at low temperature (o to 4°C). The times and centrifugal forces given in Fig. 4–3 are therefore chosen with these considerations in mind. With different tissue, different times and centrifugal forces may be applied.

It is now perhaps possible to begin to appreciate the problems which faced biologists in the 1920s, 30s, and 40s.

4.7   Elucidation of biochemical pathways—the second step

Once the successful isolation of intact organelles had been achieved, it opened the way for a series of intensive biochemical studies on isolated systems, even though work on the biochemistry of chloroplasts and mitochondria had begun somewhat earlier.

It is impossible to try to deal with all the biochemical developments between 1920 and 1950. However, we feel that certain ideas deserve mention.

In the field of photosynthesis one problem, as we have already mentioned, was the source of oxygen production. The solution was only finally achieved as a result of applying the then new technique of radioactive labelling. Another major problem centred around the first intermediate product of carbon reduction in photosynthesis. As early as 1843, the German chemist LIEBIG had proposed that plant acids were the intermediates between carbon dioxide and sugars. This theory stemmed in the main from the example of ripening fruits which are first acid and later become sweet. However, the theory was challenged and later supplanted in 1870 by BAEYER's 'formaldehyde theory'. This theory proposed that carbon dioxide was reduced to formaldehyde, after preliminary decomposition to carbon monoxide and oxygen. Formaldehyde was then condensed to form carbohydrate. Although much experimental evidence accumulated against the 'formaldehyde theory', it was not until 1948 that it was finally proved wrong. In that year, CALVIN AND BENSON using labelled $^{14}CO_2$ found that the first intermediate fixation products were in fact phosphoglyceric acid and malic acid. Their approach typifies many of the present day biochemical studies, since they reasoned that as photosynthesis was a multistep process, then by 'tagging' CO_2 and stopping the process part way after different intervals of time, the intermediates could be identified and would be 'tagged' sequentially. The early work, however, involved them in tedious extraction, precipitation, and ion exchange column procedures, but later they perfected a simpler technique using a combination of tracers ($^{14}CO_2$) and paper chromatography. This work finally led to the discovery of the Calvin cycle.

Thanks to the work of Calvin and his co-workers on 'the path of carbon in photosynthesis ('dark reaction'), and later Arnon and his co-workers (1954) on the photochemical processes ('light reaction'), the essential biochemistry of photosynthesis is now understood. However, it was the

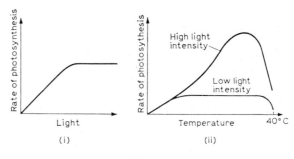

Fig. 4–4

English plant physiologist, F. F. BLACKMAN, who first drew attention to the idea of distinct 'light' and 'dark' reactions in 1905. Blackman investigated the effects of light intensity on the rate of photosynthesis, reasoning that as light energy drives photosynthesis, then the process should go faster in more intense light. His results are shown in Fig. 4–4(i). Initially, as he predicted, an increase in light production increased the rate of photosynthesis, but at higher light intensity some other factor(s) was/were rate limiting. Blackman went on to show that CO_2 concentration was one of the limiting factors, and that temperature was another (see Fig. 4–4(ii)). Not only did Blackman demonstrate the 'principle of limiting factors', but in the light/ temperature experiments he correctly deduced that photosynthesis includes both a 'light' and a 'dark' reaction, and by 'dark' he meant one which was *independent of light* but *not* necessarily carried out in darkness. Blackman's reasoning was as follows: if little light is available, then the amount of light is the factor which determines the *overall* rate of photosynthesis. However, when plenty of light is available for the light reaction, then the rate of the dark enzyme reaction determines the overall rate of photosynthesis. An increase in temperature speeds up the dark reaction and therefore the overall rate of photosynthesis (i.e. chemical reactions are temperature dependent, but light reactions are unaffected by temperature).

Further support for separate 'light' and 'dark' reactions stemmed from the experiments of HILL in the 1930s. Hill showed that when chick-weed chloroplast suspensions were illuminated, they could drive the reduction of ferricyanide or ferric oxalate, and evolve oxygen. This reaction, referred to as the 'Hill Reaction', can be used as an assay for the non-cyclic photosynthetic light reaction. In other words, isolated chloroplasts in the presence of light appear to contain part of the photosynthetic mechanism necessary for splitting water. Today we know that other hydrogen acceptors can be used, and that the light reaction is particularly important in the reduction of naturally occurring NADP, which in turn is subsequently involved in driving the carbon fixation cycle (dark reaction—see Chapter 2). It is especially interesting to note that Hill and subsequent workers found that CO_2 itself could *not* be used as a hydrogen acceptor, once again emphasizing the role of CO_2 in the dark reaction.

In the field of respiration, certain names stand out most prominently; Warburg's life-time work on respiration; KEILIN and HARTREE's work on the cytochromes, and HANS KREBS' elucidation of the tricarboxylic acid cycle. Their work was important for a number of reasons.

In the first instance, it seems that early life on earth was an anaerobic one. However, with the production of oxygen by photosynthesis, oxygen formed an atmospheric ozone layer which gave living organisms greater protection from dangerous ultraviolet irradiation. In addition, as life evolved, aerobic respiration proved to be a more efficient way of generating energy. Indeed, LOUIS PASTEUR (1861) demonstrated that cultures of yeast utilized glucose more efficiently under aerobic than anaerobic conditions, as part of the energy available from glucose breakdown remains locked up in the alcohol produced during anaerobiosis. However, if the total energy available from glucose was released all at once, it would be useless to living organisms. It was due to the work of Warburg and Keilin during the years 1923–38 that we are now able to appreciate that small quantities of chemical energy are released systematically along a chain of oxidation–reduction carriers (electrochemical gradient), in such a way that ATP is produced. ATP itself was discovered by LOHMANN (1931), and the description of oxidative phosphorylation is associated with KALCKAR (1941). Once again, it was the application of a relatively new technique, absorption spectroscopy, which solved the problem. Consequently, the basic form of the respiratory chain was known from that time to be:

Dehydrogenases $\longrightarrow$ Flavoproteins $\longrightarrow$ Cytochromes $\longrightarrow$ Oxygen

The question which Krebs and his co-workers helped to solve were these; first, where and what is the source of hydrogen donation, and second, how is the mechanism for hydrogen donation maintained?

By simple, yet penetrating experiments, Krebs was able to show that dehydrogenases were involved in a cyclic series of chemical reactions associated exclusively with mitochondria. The feature of this cycle is that a 6C acid (citric acid) is oxidized to a 4C acid (oxalacetic acid), but the fact that it is a cyclic rather than a linear sequence of chemical events means that the system is self-perpetuating. The Krebs cycle, rather like a conveyor belt, is a much more efficient way of distributing potential energy to the electron transport chain, provided that it is in the first place constantly supplied with a food source. In addition, the cycle is self-regulating, since from our conveyor-belt analogy, the 'build up' of any one component either speeds up or slows down the cycle until the 'bottle neck' is removed.

In retrospect then, we see that early studies into the problems of photosynthesis and respiration stemmed from an interest in the restoration of respired air by plants. Indeed, in many textbooks, attention has been drawn to the fact that photosynthesis is the reverse of respiration. This is true in so far as the initial products of one reaction are the end products of the other, but from biochemical studies we now know that there is an important unifying process in both—*this is the production of ATP*. In photosynthesis, ATP is produced by photophosphorylation, and in respiration it is produced by oxidative phosphorylation. In both cases, the chemical energy produced is necessary for doing work. The generation of ATP in the first instance is vital to drive the production of sugars and eventually other organic substances, and in the second instance, ATP is essential for animals and plants to carry out all of their physiological functions. In this respect, recent research has shown that ATP is not only involved in the energetics of biochemical pathways, but also in controlling the rate of several of the enzymic steps in these pathways (allosteric control). Pasteur's observations, for example (p. 51), can now be explained in terms of the allosteric control exerted on certain enzymes by varying concentrations of ATP.

4.8   The introduction of the electron microscope—a new era in cell biology

With the first electron micrographs of chloroplasts in 1940 by KAUSCHE and RUSKA, and the first high resolution electron micrographs of mitochondria by Sjöstrand and Palade independently in 1952–53, a new era in cell biology was opened. It now became possible to analyse the fine structure of these organelles, and at last the way was open for investigations into the molecular organization of multienzyme systems within distinct morphological units.

At this point, it seems appropriate to turn our attention to the new developments in chloroplast and mitochondrial research, and thus to close this chapter.

Origin and Assembly of Chloroplasts and Mitochondria

5.1 Introduction

The previous chapters have outlined the involvement of chloroplasts and mitochondria in the energy metabolism of living organisms.

The complexity of the processes involved in energy metabolism and the dependence of these processes on a highly ordered structure has stimulated interest in the problem of how these organelles are assembled. The results obtained by research workers in this field suggest that in addition to those components normally concerned in the synthesis of enzymes, i.e. nuclear DNA, messenger RNA, transfer RNA, and ribosomes (see § 5.3), there is also a duplicate set of these constituents, located within and specific to the organelle in question. The problem is complicated by the lack of general agreement concerning the cellular origin of the organelles, (this is particularly so in the case of mitochondria). The presence within chloroplasts and mitochondria of their own DNA, RNA and protein synthesizing apparatus has also led to speculation concerning the origin of the organelles. This last chapter concerns itself with these problems in an attempt to indicate one of the main directions in which research into chloroplasts and mitochondria is progressing.

5.2 The cellular origin of chloroplasts and mitochondria

It is obviously impossible to arrive at a definitive answer to the question 'How are chloroplasts and mitochondria assembled?' until one has a good idea of where in the cell these organelles originate. Although considerable research has been put into this problem, the answer is still by no means clear. In unicellular green plants (algae) there is fairly convincing electron microscopic evidence that chloroplasts can divide. In higher plants, however, there is scant evidence for the division of mature chloroplasts. Instead the chloroplasts appear to develop from much smaller, relatively undifferentiated bodies which have been termed proplastids. Consequently, whereas the continuity of chloroplasts in algae appears to be maintained by division, the continuity in higher plants is probably maintained by division of the proplastids.

The corresponding problem of mitochondrial origin is still more complex. Electron micrographs have once again produced evidence that in a large number of species mitochondria can divide, and observations in the phase-contrast microscope show that rat liver mitochondria are continuously dividing and coalescing. However, in yeasts there is evidence that mitochondria originate from promitochondria. Like the proplastids the promitochondria are smaller and less organized than the mature organelles. Again, other workers in this field have published electron micrographs in which the mitochondrial membrane is continuous with the nuclear or cell membrane or endoplasmic reticulum, and claim that these represent mitochondria in the process of formation by vesiculation of a part of one of these membranes.

As stated previously, it is important to bear in mind that interpretations given to electron micrographs achieve a much more solid foundation if they are supported by biochemical or genetical evidence. As we shall see (§ 5.3) this type of evidence supports the idea that at least part of the genetic information necessary for the synthesis of chloroplasts and mitochondria resides in the organelles themselves and that this information is passed onto new organelles during the division of chloroplasts and mitochondria (or proplastids and promitochondria).

5.3   The assembly of chloroplasts and mitochondria

Up until the last few years, it was generally assumed that the total information necessary for the synthesis of a cell resided in the DNA of the nucleus. The discoveries that chloroplasts and mitochondria contained their own specific DNA's, with physical properties differing from those of nuclear DNA, led to the questioning of this assumption. Before it could be accepted that these newly discovered DNA species played a part in the assembly of the organelles it was necessary to establish that:

(i) there was sufficient DNA present to be able to code for some of the chloroplast and mitochondrial proteins.

(ii) that the properties of the DNA were in accordance with its having a genetic function.

In general, chloroplasts contain approximately 5×10^{-15} g of DNA/chloroplast. It seems probable that this is divided into a number of units which may contain identical genetic information, and it has been calculated that a unit could probably code for approximately 3000 different small proteins. On the other hand, mitochondria contain much less DNA than chloroplasts. However, a more precise calculation of the information capacity of mitochondrial DNA is possible because it is generally circular, being about 5 μm in circumference. This amount of DNA is known to be capable of carrying information for the synthesis of approximately 30 small proteins. Thus the DNA present in chloroplasts and mitochondria could play a significant role in the assembly of these organelles.

That the DNA present in chloroplasts and mitochondria is likely to play such a role, is supported by both biochemical and genetical evidence. The elements necessary for the expression of the information are all present. Both organelles possess the enzymes necessary to duplicate the DNA (i.e. DNA polymerase) and to copy it onto molecules of messenger RNA (i.e. RNA polymerase). The ribosomes present within the organelles (distinguishable from those outside on the basis of their smaller size), and specific t-RNA molecules, provide the mechanism whereby the messenger RNA base sequence may be translated into proteins with specific amino acid sequences.

Mutants with faulty chloroplast or mitochondrial function can also be isolated and the mutations can be shown to be of two kinds:

(i) Those mutations whose inheritance is typical of a chromosomal gene.
(ii) Those whose inheritance is not typical of a chromosomal gene (i.e. non-chromosomal or cytoplasmic inheritance).

In the latter cases, examination of the DNA present in the faulty organelle almost always shows that it is either grossly altered or lost. Although this does not prove that damage to or loss of 'chloroplast or mitochondrial' DNA results in a loss of function, it is good evidence in its favour.

Having established that the DNA can probably provide some information for organelle assembly, the question is 'What precisely does the chloroplast or mitochondrial DNA code for?' Unfortunately, it is easier, at the present time to say, what each DNA does not code for. Investigations on the mutations inherited in a classical Mendelian pattern (chromosomal mutations) suggest that *nuclear* DNA codes for the soluble enzymes of the carbon reduction cycle, the tricarboxylic acid cycle, and also the electron carriers of both organelles. However, one cannot rule out the possibility that these proteins are assembled within the organelle on the chloroplast or mitochondrial ribosomes, using information carried from the nucleus on messenger RNA. This possibility nevertheless is unlikely as isolated organelles are unable to incorporate radioactively labelled amino acids into the soluble enzymes and cytochrome *c*.

Non-chromosomal mutations usually lead to a gross alteration in the nature of the chloroplast or mitochondrion. Usually a number of the electron transfer components and pigments are missing—even ones which are almost certainly coded for by nuclear DNA. There are two main possibilities for the information content of the chloroplast or mitochondrial DNA which can explain the gross changes resulting from the loss of this information. One possibility is that the DNA contains the information for the synthesis of the chloroplast or mitochondrial ribosomes and that the absence of these prevents the synthesis of those electron carriers which are assembled within the organelle. This idea is supported by the observation of BRAWERMANN (1963), that non-chromosomal mutants of *Euglena* with faulty chloroplasts, appear to lack chloroplast ribosomes. The second possibility is that the DNA carries information for the synthesis of the insoluble structural protein of the chloroplast thylakoid and mitochondrial inner membrane. These proteins are postulated to form the framework for the assembly of electron carriers in their functional order. Recent evidence with yeast mitochondria indicates that mitochondrial DNA codes for small subunit proteins associated with both the cytochrome oxidase and ATP-ase complex of enzymes. Figure 5-1 summarizes the present knowledge on the genetic control of mitochondrial assembly. Inevitably this picture will be rapidly superseded as more data become available.

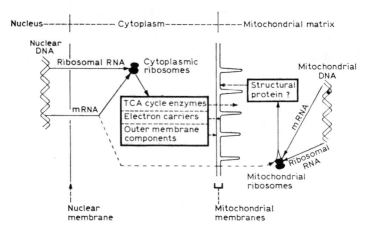

Fig. 5–1   Control of mitochondrial assembly.

It is important to realize, as in all genetical problems, that the chromosomal and non-chromosomal genes do not dictate the absolute nature of the finished product. This is modified by environmental factors and in chloroplasts and mitochondria these are particularly important. Probably the most important environmental factor in chloroplast development is light. In its absence the grana and lamellae do not form and chlorophyll synthesis does not take place. Mineral deficiency results in similar effects.

Similarly the development of mitochondria from promitochondria in yeasts is dependent upon the presence of oxygen and the absence of high levels of the sugars sucrose or glucose.

5.4   Evolutionary origin of chloroplasts and mitochondria

The discovery of growth and division of chloroplasts and mitochondria, and the presence of quite distinct DNA and protein synthesizing systems within these organelles, has brought about a renewed interest in their evolutionary origin. A number of workers have suggested that these organelles might have evolved from independent organisms which originally invaded the host cell and set up an endosymbiotic relationship with it. It can be argued that as cells became larger, the photosynthetic or respiratory activity associated with the plasma membrane alone, was insufficient to meet ATP requirements. It is possible that in exchange for the equable surroundings of the host cell, the symbionts provided additional photosynthetic or respiratory assemblies to manufacture more ATP. In the case of chloroplasts, the invading organism is considered to be similar to blue-green algae. These acellular organisms, which do not contain chloroplasts, are capable of photosynthesis by means of photosynthetic assemblies located on the lamellae and which ramify throughout the whole organism. Mitochondria on the other hand, are considered to have evolved from symbiotic bacteria. In bacteria, which do not contain mitochondria, the electron transfer and phosphorylating systems are located on the limiting membrane of the organism. There are two major difficulties. The first is that considerable readjustment in the way of life of these organisms would have been necessary if they were to give up most (if not all) of the synthesized ATP to the host cell. Perhaps as in certain families of bacteria (Rickettsiae) which parasitize insect cells, the host is necessary to provide certain essential glycolytic substrates, so that oxidative phosphorylation can take place. The other objection is that more than one strain of blue-green alga or bacterium would be expected to be an 'infective' symbiont. This means that one might anticipate much greater heterogeneity in chloroplasts and mitochondrial populations than appears to occur.

The alternative to the endosymbiont theory for the origin of chloroplasts and mitochondria would be that they evolved (de novo) within the cell itself in response to a higher demand for photosynthetic and respiratory activity. Although experimental evidence does not favour a de novo origin, there is no compelling evidence to support either theory. However, over the last few years a number of interesting observations have tended to favour the endosymbiotic theory.

Firstly, the fact that mitochondrial DNA has been shown to be in the form of circular molecules, parallels the presence of circular DNA in bacteria. Secondly, the ribosomes in chloroplasts and mitochondria are smaller than those of the cytoplasm in the same organism and more nearly equivalent to the size of ribosomes in blue-green algae and bacteria. The most compelling evidence, however, is concerned with the sensitivity to antibiotics of the protein synthesizing systems in the cytoplasm, in mitochondria, and in bacteria. These are summarized in Table 4.

Table 4

	Cytoplasmic	Mitochondrial	Bacterial
Cycloheximide	+	—	—
Chloramphenicol	—	+	+
Erythromycin	—	+	+

+ = inhibition   — = no inhibition

This emphasizes the similarity between the protein synthesizing systems of mitochondria and bacteria.

We are therefore presented with a very challenging problem, one in fact of many problems facing biochemists and cell physiologists in this field. It is unlikely that the evolutionary origin of chloroplasts and mitochondria will be resolved, although it is nice to speculate, but the answers to many of the other problems which we have pointed to, although difficult to obtain, will eventually be common knowledge.

Suggestions for Practical Work

It is not particularly easy to recommend interesting yet suitable practical work for introductory classes, which at the same time illustrates some of the important properties of chloroplasts and mitochondria. We realize that school resources are limited and that some schools are better endowed with equipment than others, so that potentially they may be capable of more elaborate experimentation. However, with these problems in mind we have suggested certain practical schedules which can be performed with the minimum amount of equipment. The most important general precaution to remember when isolating chloroplasts or mitochondria is to keep reagents and vessels cold (i.e. 0–4°C).

6.1 Chloroplasts

Chloroplasts can be isolated by grinding the leaves of spinach, chickweed or sugar beet in cold 0.35M NaCl and 0.02M Phosphate buffer (pH 8). The grinding (approximately 2 or 3 leaves) can be carried out in a pestle and mortar by mixing a small quantity of sand to the leaves and the isolation medium. The mixture is then squeezed through four layers of boiled muslin, which has been soaked in cold isolation medium, and collected in a centrifuge tube. The green liquid obtained is spun in a bench centrifuge at low speed (100–$200 \times$ g) for 1–2 minutes to sediment cell debris. The supernatant from this spin is centrifuged at top speed on the bench centrifuge for 8–10 minutes (the centrifugal force ideally should be about $2000 \times$ g). The pellet of chloroplasts obtained is then resuspended in a small volume (1–2 ml) of buffered 0.35M NaCl.

This preparation can be used to study the Hill reaction (see Chapter 4, p. 51). In this reaction the reduction of an added dye DCPIP (2,6-dichlorophenolindophenol) can be used instead of NADPH which occurs physiologically.

Add 0.1 ml of the chloroplast suspension to 5 ml of 10^{-4}M DCPIP. On illumination the blue DCPIP will be reduced to the colourless "leuco"-form of the dye. An unilluminated control should be prepared at the same time. The time taken to discharge the blue colour is an indication of the activity of the non-cyclic electron transfer system. This assay can be used to investigate the relative efficiency of different wavelengths of light and different intensities of light.

6.2 Mitochondria

Of all the different sources of mitochondria, probably the largest and easiest to isolate are those from the thoracic flight muscles of blowflies.

40–50 flies are immobilized by keeping them on ice at 0–4°C. The heads, wings, and abdomina are quickly removed, and the thoraces collected in a cold mortar containing isolation medium. A suitable isolation medium is cold 0.32M sucrose buffered with 0.02M Tris/HCl (or phosphate) at pH 7.3, containing 0.01M EDTA (sodium salt of ethylenediamine tetra-acetic acid) and 1 per cent bovine serum albumin. The thoraces are gently pulped for two minutes (*avoid grinding or adding sand*) and the mixture squeezed in cold centrifuge tubes through four layers of boiled muslin washed in cold isolation medium. After a low spin (100 × g) for 2 minutes to remove cell debris, the supernatant is spun at top speed in a bench centrifuge (preferably 2500 × g) for 10 minutes. The mitochondrial pellet is resuspended in 1–2 ml of fresh isolation medium.

Again, the mitochondrial preparation can be used to study the reduction of an indo-phenol dye (e.g. DCPIP), seen as a change from a blue colouration to the colourless form. This reaction which takes place in the absence of light may be compared with the Hill reaction mentioned above. The requirements are 0.1 ml mitochondria in buffered isolation medium, 5 ml of 10^{-4}M DCPIP and 0.1 ml of 0.03M succinate or DL-α-glycerophosphate. Reduction of the dye takes place between succinate or α-glycerophosphate and flavoprotein in the respiratory chain. A control without substrate should be used. Students might also like to make a comparison between the supernatant and the particulate fractions of both chloroplast and mitochondrial preparations to see where greatest activity is found.

In addition if schools possess Warburg flasks and manometers, O_2 uptake of mitochondria can be easily measured. Again it is possible to demonstrate phosphorylation in mitochondria by measuring phosphate uptake, but precautions should be taken to see that an ATP 'trapping system' is present in the reaction medium (i.e. ADP, glucose, and the enzyme hexokinase). Details of these more sophisticated techniques together with advice on isolating other types of mitochondria can be obtained from the following references:

Manometric Techniques, Ed. Umbreit, Burris & Stauffer (Burgess Publishing Co.).
Experimental Biochemistry, Clark (Freeman & Co.).
Methods in Enzymology, $\bar{X}$—Oxidation and phosphorylation, Colowick & Kaplan Academic Press, New York.
An experimental approach to biology, Abramoff and Thomson (Freeman) 1966.

Further Reading

BARKER, G. (1969). *Understanding the Chemistry of the Cell*, Edward Arnold, London.

BRANTON, D. (1969). 'Membrane structure'. *Annual Review of Plant Physiology* **20**, 209–37.

FOGG, G. E. (1968). *Photosynthesis*, E.U.P., London.

GOODENOUGH, U. W. and LEVINE, R. P. (1970). 'The genetic activity of mitochondria and chloroplasts'. *Scientific American*, **223**, 22–9.

GRIMSTONE, A. V. (1968). *The Electron Microscope in Biology*. Edward Arnold, London.

HALL, D. O. and RAO, K. K. (1972). *Photosynthesis*, Edward Arnold, London.

KIRK, J. T. and TILNEY-BASSETT, R. A. E. (1967). *The Plastids*, W. H. Freeman, London.

LEHNINGER, A. L. (1961). 'How cells transform energy'. *Scientific American* **205**, 62–7.

LEHNINGER, A. L. (1964). *The Mitochondrion*. Benjamin, N.Y.

LEHNINGER, A. L. (1965). *Bioenergetics*, Benjamin, N.Y.

LEVINE, R. P. (1969). 'The mechanism of photosynthesis'. *Scientific American*, **221**, 58–71.

RABINOWITZ, M. and SWIFT, H. (1970). 'Mitochondrial nucleic acids and their relation to the biogenisis of mitochondria'. *Physiological Reviews*, **50**, 376–427.

RACKER, E. (1968). 'The membrane of the mitochondrion'. *Scientific American* **218**, 32–9.

RACKER, E. (1969). *Membranes of mitochondria and chloroplasts*, Van Nostrand.

RACKER, E. (1970). 'The two faces of the inner mitochondrial membrane'. *Essays in Biochemistry* **6**, 1–22.

ROBERTSON, R. N. (1968). *Protons, Electrons, Phosphorylation and Active Transport*, Cambridge University Press.

ROODYN, D. B. and WILKIE, D. (1968). *Biogenesis of Mitochondria*, Methuen, London.